AIRCRAFT MAINTENANCE MANAGEMENT

AIRCRAFT MAINTENANCE MANAGEMENT

C. H. FRIEND

Longman
Scientific &
Technical

Longman Scientific & Technical,
Longman Group UK Limited,
Longman House, Burnt Mill, Harlow,
Essex CM20 2JE, England
and Associated Companies throughout the world.

First published 1992

British Library Cataloguing in Publication Data
A catalogue record for this book is available from the
British Library
ISBN 0-582-03866-9

Set in Compugraphic $9\frac{1}{2}$/12pt Times

Printed in Singapore
by Longman Singapore Publishers (Pte) Ltd

To Ken Wilkinson

CONTENTS

FOREWORD

All forms of public transport are unforgiving of safety management deficiencies which continue to be tragically demonstrated on the sea, on the railways, as well as in the air. Aviation is particularly vulnerable, be it an airline or a small air taxi operator.

Regulations and requirements only form the basis for safety management in which maintenance is a major element; they do not, in themselves, achieve it. The introduction of harmonised requirements under the Joint Aviation Authority will have an important impact on the application of common maintenance standards throughout Europe; they may well also be adopted as regulatory standards by other nations.

The need to demonstrate corporate and personal responsibility has never been higher; commitment to safety must be demonstrated and become part of an organisation's ethos, with continual review and determination to maintain its prominent position. All too frequently we see situations which cause us to ask ourselves the question 'how could that have possibly been allowed to happen?' It was obvious. It is still very often the simple things that let us down, not the high technology, although this, in itself, can lead to complacency. Safety management has a crucial part to play in relation to this question, particularly in the competitive situation which aviation finds itself today as the world passes into an ever increasing deregulated environment.

The financial position of operators tends to have wide swings of fortune to which management needs to be able to react to keep up with the situation. The regulatory rules are the source of minimum standards; however, it is the operator's responsibility to maintain a safe operation at all times as the holder of an air operator's certificate or its equivalent international approval.

Continued airworthiness is a truly international affair, being the discipline of ensuring the integrity of an aircraft throughout its life. The development of more detailed procedures and intended standards have been receiving attention from ICAO, the European JAA and the FAA which will continue to provide further focus at international levels. The regulatory authorities are faced with an ever increasing task of ensuring that safety standards are maintained on aircraft, ranging from pre-World War II piston engine types to the fly-by-wire, technically sophisticated jets. The feedback of defect data to the responsible manufacturer or type certificate holder is vital, as is their willingness and ability to act upon the data in conjunction with the regulatory authority concerned. Good relations are crucial to success between manufacturers, operators and regulatory authorities alike, as has been recently highlighted by the remarkable co-operation levels of all interested groups concerned with the structural integrity of ageing jet fleets. However, it is not good enough to wait until the needs become urgent; more effort is required to keep abreast of problems being identified by assessments of inspections and defect data. Action must be taken earlier rather than later, even though it may be to the detriment of commercial plans.

Foreword

The world-wide large transport aircraft fatal accident rates have shown a dramatic improvement over the past 30 years; however, they have now largely flattened out and it is obvious that, as air transport movements increase, the safety standards must continue to improve, in order to maintain the same accident rate; a further improvement will be required to reduce this accident rate. Some five per cent of large transport aeroplane accidents are directly attributable to maintenance errors, the remaining fifteen per cent of accidents, due to airworthiness causal factors, have often involved a measure of identifiable maintenance error. Helicopters, by definition, are more vulnerable to airworthiness causal accidents due to their single load path critical systems, and the airworthiness causal factor rates are assessed as being approximately double that for the fixed-wing transports. Clearly, there is a need for improvement in the safety management of maintenance activities.

Human factors in maintenance are receiving more attention than ever before; however, it is still relatively in its infancy compared with that of the work carried out for flight operations, and more effort is required on this important aspect. Maintenance training is often a primary target for financial pruning action and such cuts have led to a severe shortage of qualified maintenance staff in recent years; the industry cannot afford to cut back on its investment in human technical resources if it is to ensure that the required high standards of maintenance are to be achieved.

Very few books have been written on aircraft maintenance management. I strongly encouraged the writing of this volume by Dr C. H. Friend under the editorship of Mr D. H. Middleton. Its very contents give a clear indication of the many aspects which need to be given consideration; aircraft maintenance is a complex interactive matter and the study of the text of this book will assist in a better understanding of aircraft maintenance and the control of operational standards.

John W. Saull
Head of Operating Standards Division
Civil Aviation Authority

PREFACE

Among the many people who have provided useful information and assistance in producing this book, I would like to thank the following:

Don Middleton, editor of this series, for organising visits and supervision, and Longman books.

Don Craig, British Airways; John Saull, Civil Aviation Authority; and David Yeomans, Cranfield Institute of Technology, for encouraging the start of this project.

Ken Wagner, British Airways; Jim Rainbow, John Gibson, Roy Wyer, of Monarch Aircraft Engineering for discussions.

AVM K A Campbell RAF, AOC Maintenance Units, for assistance in making visits to RAF stations possible. Sqn Ldr C A Elkins, Sqn Ldr V Driver, Flt Lt D Smith, of CSDE RAF Swanton Morley. Sqn Ldr M J Kilshaw, RAF Abingdon. Air Cdre D R French, Station Commander; Gp Capt P Turfery, S Admin O; Wg Cdr P B Morell, OC Supply Wing; at RAF St Athan. Station Commander and J D Edwards, at No 30 MU RAF Sealand. Mr S H Clarke, MoD Publications Clearance Branch.

Students of the City University Air Transport Engineering Course for information, reports, and insight into the workings of the industry.

C H Friend
April 1992

ABBREVIATIONS

ABBREVIATIONS USED — GENERAL

£	UK pound sterling
$	US dollar
AAIB	Air Accident Investigation Branch, UK Dept of Transport
ACARS	aircraft communication and reporting system
AD	Airworthiness Directive
ADES	avionic direct exchange scheme
AECMA	Association Européenne des Constructeurs de Matériel Aérospatial
AIDS	airborne integrated data system
AMS	Approved Maintenance Schedule
ANO	Air Navigation Order (UK)
AOC	air operator's certificate
APU	auxiliary power unit
AQAP	Allied Quality Assurance Publication (NATO)
ARINC	Aeronautical Radio Inc.
ASB	alert service bulletin
ASK	available seat-kilometres
ATA	Air Transport Association (USA)
AVM	airborne vibration monitoring
BA	British Airways plc
BAe	British Aerospace plc
BCAR	British Civil Airworthiness Requirements
billion	1,000 million (equal to European milliard)
BITE	built-in test equipment
C of A	Certificate of Airworthiness
CAA	Civil Aviation Authority (UK)
CFC	carbon fibre composite
CFM	joint engine company of GE (USA) and SNECMA (France)
CMC	central maintenance computer
CMR	Certificate of Maintenance Review (UK CAA)
CPA	critical path analysis
CSDE	Central Servicing Development Establishment (RAF)
DOC	direct operating cost
DoT	Department of Transport (UK)
E&M	engineering and maintenance
EC	European Commission, European Community
ECAC	European Conference on Civil Aviation

ECM	engine condition monitoring
EFA	European fighter aircraft project
EGT	exhaust gas temperature
EICAS	engine indication and crew alert system
EROPS	Extended-Range Operations
ETOPS	Extended-Range Twin Operations
FAA	Fleet Air Arm (UK)
FAA	Federal Aviation Administration (USA)
FADEC	full-authority digital engine control
FAR	Federal Airworthiness Regulations (USA)
FD	flight director (a cockpit instrument)
FDR	flight data recorder
FMCS	flight management computer system
GE	General Electric Company (engine manufacturer)
GPWS	ground proximity warning system
HP	high pressure (usually in turbine engines)
hr	hours
HUMS	health and usage monitoring system
IATA	International Air Transport Association
ICAO	International Civil Aviation Organisation
IFSD	inflight shutdown rate
ILS	instrument landing system
INS	inertial navigation system
IP	intermediate pressure (of three-shaft turbine engines)
IT	information technology
JAA	Joint Aviation Authority (Europe)
JAR	Joint Aviation Requirement
LCF	low cycle fatigue
LP	low pressure
LRU	line replaceable unit
LWTR	licence without type rating (UK CAA)
M	million $(1,000,000 = 10^6)$
MACD	Maintenance Analysis and Computing Division (RAF, 1990)
M&O	maintenance and overhaul
MACE	Maintenance Analysis and Computing Establishment (RAF)
MDC	Maintenance Data Centre (RAF)
MEL	Minimum Equipment List
MMEL	Master Minimum Equipment List
MoD	Ministry of Defence (UK)
MPD	Maintenance Planning Document
MRP	material resource planning
MRP II	manufacturing resource planning
MSG-3	Maintenance Steering Group — 3
MSI	maintenance significant item
MTBF	mean time between failures
MTBUR	mean time between unscheduled removals
MTOW	maximum take-off weight
MTWA	maximum total weight authorised
MU	Maintenance Unit (RAF usage)
NATO	North Atlantic Treaty Organisation
NDI	non-destructive inspection

NDT	non-destructive testing
NPRM	Notice of Proposed Rule Making (US FAA)
NTSB	National Transportation Safety Board (USA)
OSI	Open Systems Interconnection (a computer standard)
P&W	Pratt and Whitney (engine manufacturers)
PERT	programme evaluation and review technique
RAF	Royal Air Force (UK)
R&M	reliability and maintenance
RCM	Reliability Centered Maintenance (USA)
RPK	revenue passenger-kilometre
RR	Rolls-Royce plc (engine manufacturer)
SB	service bulletin
SEMA	Station Engineering Management Aid (RAF)
SI	Servicing Instruction (RAF)
SOAP	spectrometric oil analysis programme
SSI	structural significant item
SSID	Supplementary Structural Inspection Document (US FAA)
SSIP	Supplemental Structural Inspection Program (US FAA)
STI	special technical instructions (RAF)
TIT	turbine inlet temperature
UK	United Kingdom of Great Britain and Northern Ireland
US, USA	United States of America

ABBREVIATIONS OFTEN USED FOR AIRCRAFT

A300	Airbus Industrie A300 series twinjet wide-body airliner
B727	Boeing model 727 trijet narrow-body airliner
B737	Boeing model 737 twin jet narrow-body airliner
B747	Boeing model 747 four jet wide-body airliner
B757	Boeing model 757 twin jet narrow-body airliner
B767	Boeing model 767 twin jet wide-body airliner
DC-8	McDonnell Douglas DC8 four jet narrow-body airliner
DC-9	McDonnell Douglas DC9 twin jet narrow-body airliner
DC-10	McDonnell Douglas DC10 trijet wide-body airliner
L1011	Lockheed model 1011 (TriStar) trijet wide-body airliner
MD-80	McDonnell Douglas MD-80 series twin jet narrow-body airliner
MD-11	McDonnell Douglas MD-11 trijet wide-body airliner

ABBREVIATIONS OFTEN USED BY OTHER OPERATORS

KLM	Koninklijke Luchtvaart Maatschappij (KLM Royal Dutch Airlines)
SAS	Scandinavian Airlines System
TWA	Trans World Airlines (USA)
UAL	United Air Lines (USA)
UTA	Union de Transporte Aériens
VARIG	Viação Aérea Rio-Grandense (Brazil)

CHAPTER 1 AIRWORTHINESS AND ITS REGULATION

THE AIR SAFETY RECORD

Air transport is now a very safe way of travelling, despite the media attention given to air accidents. Measured by the usual statistics of risk per unit of exposure, such as accidents per trip or fatalities per passenger-kilometre, air transport compares well with most other modes.

A summary of the recent world civil air transport fatal accident record is shown in Table 1.1 and Fig. 1.1 (from ICAO, published in *Flight International*). The statistics exclude cases of sabotage, hijacking and military action, on the grounds that these are 'non-air transport' events of political origin. From these it is apparent that an average of around 1,000 fatalities a year over ten years occurred to air travellers worldwide. In comparison, it should be noted that road casualties in Great Britain alone (a country with a relatively low road accident rate by European standards) amount to just over 5,000 killed per year, with many more seriously injured. Fatality rates for different modes of transport are compared in Fig. 1.2.

The world trend in total fatalities shows a slight rise over the past ten years. However, the fatality rate has declined because traffic growth has been at a much greater rate; the effect, over the past 20 years, is shown in Figs 1.3 and 1.4. Although the improvement is welcome, the historical annual decline in accidents per departure

Table 1.1 Civil air transport fatalities and accidents (excludes sabotage, hijack, military action)

Year	Total fatalities	Total accidents	Non-Soviet bloc		Soviet bloc	
			Fatalities	Accidents	Fatalities	Accidents
1981	710	29	461	26	249	3
1982	1,012	33	773	28	239	5
1983	1,202	34	1,160	31	42	3
1984	451	29	251	27	200	2
1985	1,800	39	1,564	33	236	6
1986	607	31	529	28	78	3
1987	834	28	695	25	183	2
1988	1,007	54	943	49	64	5
1989	1,450	51	1,223	46	227	5
1990	611	35	535	30	76	5
Average	1,031	43	879	38	152	5

Plate 1 Hangar at Hong Kong Aircraft Engineering Co. (HAECO)

Fig. 1.1 World total air accidents and trend

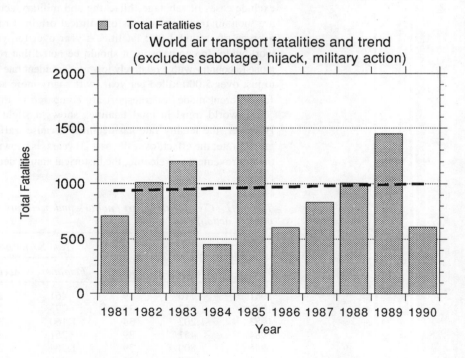

is about the same value as that quoted for the rate of increase in forecast journeys, hence the nearly static value of total accidents is expected to continue. This assumes that improvements in safety, equal to those made in the past, can be continued in future, and some industry experts have doubted that this will be possible because many obvious accident causes have now been tackled.

Fig. 1.2 UK transport fatality rates

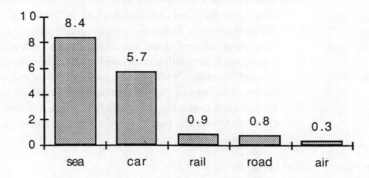

UK deaths per billion pasgr-km 1976–87

Fig. 1.3 World accident rate trend

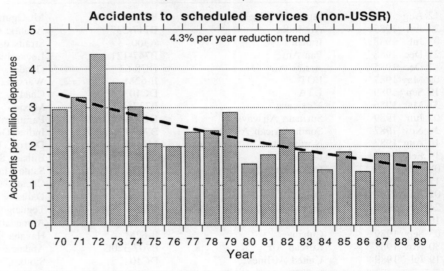

☐ Accidents per million departures

Fig. 1.4 World fatality rate trend

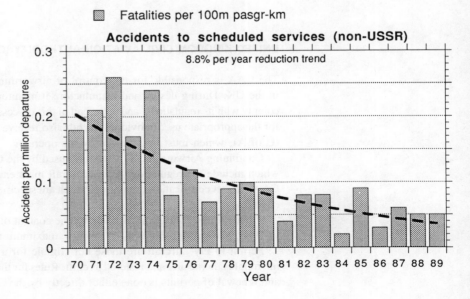

☐ Fatalities per 100m pasgr-km

As the number of wide-bodied aircraft in service grows, it can be expected that more accidents will involve large aircraft. The worst 20 civil air transport accidents of the past five years are summarised in Table 1.2. Those in this list were due to different causes, including airline-related ones such as flying and engineering procedures, as well as the non-airline causes such as sabotage and military/political action. Accidents with a great number of fatalities have a perceptible impact on travel demand immediately afterwards, especially if there is public disquiet expressed about the possible causes. The international nature of air transport also makes the ensuing legal process expensive and lengthy. The industry must therefore make every possible effort to reduce the potential for aircraft accidents and fatalities.

Table 1.2   Worst 20 air transport accidents 1985—1989

Date	Carrier	Aircraft	Location	Fatalities
12 Aug 1985	Japan Air Lines	B747	Mt Ogura, Japan	520
23 Jun 1985	Air India	B747-237	Atlantic Ocean	329
03 Jul 1988	Iranair	A300	Straits of Hormuz	290
21 Dec 1988	Pan Am	B747-121	Lockerbie, Scotland	259
12 Dec 1985	Arrow Air	DC8-63	Gander, NF	256
09 May 1987	LOT	Il-62M	Warsaw	183
19 Sep 1989	UTA	DC10	Chad	171
31 Mar 1986	Mexicana	B727	Mexico	167
07 Jun 1989	Surinam Airways	DC8-62	Paramaribo	166
28 Nov 1987	South African Airways	B747 Combi	Indian Ocean	160
16 Aug 1987	Northwest	MD-82	Detroit, MI	152
19 Feb 1985	Iberia	B727	Bilbao, Spain	148
08 Feb 1989	Independent Air	B707	Santa Maria, Azores	144
17 Mar 1988	Avianca	B727	Cúcuta, Colombia	139
02 Aug 1985	Delta	TriStar	Dallas	136
21 Oct 1989	Sabsa	B727	Tegucigalpa, Honduras	131
19 Oct 1988	Indian Airlines	B737-200	Ahmedabad, India	130
03 Sep 1989	Cubana	Il-62M	Havana	126
30 Nov 1987	Korean Air	B707-320C	Andaman Sea	115
19 Jul 1989	United Airlines	DC10	Sioux City, Iowa	111

UNITED KINGDOM CIVIL AVIATION AUTHORITY (CAA)

The CAA is responsible for the control of airworthiness for all aircraft registered in the UK. During design and manufacture it monitors aircraft to ensure that they comply with its regulations, and at the end of this process the aircraft type is certificated for the appropriate use. Individual aircraft also receive a Certificate of Airworthiness (C of A), which must be renewed by the operator.

'Continuing Airworthiness' is the term used by the CAA to describe its activities, which include the regulation of civil aircraft maintenance. Table 1.3 gives the UK CAA aircraft certification categories, which are specified in the Air Navigation Order (ANO).

A guide to the CAA work is given by the content of the UK civil aircraft register in 1986, shown in Table 1.4 (MTWA = maximum total weight authorised).

'Permit to Fly' aircraft are those not eligible for a normal C of A, and include microlights, homebuilt and restored aircraft. Rules for their maintenance are simplified, and renewal of permits is done either directly by the CAA or devolved to a suitable

United Kingdom Civil Aviation Authority (CAA)

Table 1.3   UK CAA aircraft certification categories

Description	Aircraft in 1987
1. Transport Category (Passenger)	2,654
2. Transport Category (Cargo)	7
3. Aerial Work Category (includes balloons)	698
4. Private Category	2,798
5. Special Category	108
6. Permit to Fly	1,229

Table 1.4   UK civil aircraft register by categories

Aeroplanes over 5,700 kg MTWA	575
Aeroplanes from 2,730 to 5,700 kg MTWA	437
Aeroplanes below 2,730 kg MTWA	5,411
Helicopters	566
Balloons and airships	611
Total	7,600
Permit to Fly, includes 504 microlights	1,229
Total of types and variants	1,915

volunteer organisation, such as the Popular Flying Association (PFA). Other such societies cater for other branches of private flying. Special Category aircraft are those not fully meeting current requirements, usually prototypes.

Private Category aircraft exceeding 2,730 kg (was 6,000 lb) MTWA do not require an approved maintenance schedule; these are usually business aircraft kept by large companies. Aircraft and helicopters below 2,730 kg MTWA are covered by the light aircraft maintenance schedule (LAMS); this is a simplified scheme with a three-year cycle.

The bulk of CAA administrative work is thus concentrated on the heavier transport and aerial work categories. The Air Navigation Order Article 6 requires all UK transport operators to hold an Air Operator's Certificate (AOC), issued by the CAA Operations Division (see p. 11). Maintenance organisation requirements for this are described in CAP 360, which gives general and specific advice on structure and operation for aircraft engineering support. The CAA lays great stress on the need for adequate recording and analysis of work done on aircraft, since it is through such data that the CAA can check the adequacy of this work.

There are over 200 AOC holders, but about 150 of these are minor operators with aircraft below 5,700 kg (12,500 lb) MTWA. This may increase as moves to European deregulation of air transport encourage more operators to enter the market.

There are three different maintenance schemes in use by operators; these are:

1. The M1 Maintenance Approval scheme, with corporate responsibility, suitable for large operators with heavier aircraft. Staff with qualifications below a full licence may be used in inspection and maintenance, but a sampling quality control system is required.
2. The B1 Overhaul Approval scheme, with licensed engineer and approved inspector, suitable for any aircraft.
3. The M3 Maintenance Approval scheme, with licensed engineers, suitable for smaller aircraft below 2,730 kg MTWA.

The CAA monitors the operator's actual maintenance standards by ensuring that area office staff sample at least 10 per cent of the register annually, for maintenance work from ramp servicing up to major overhaul. Data from these surveys are fed into a trend monitoring program.

The corporate responsibility scheme with M1 approval gives the operator more control over maintenance and scheduling, but also more responsibility. The CAA monitors performance, for which the operator must also have an approved internal quality control programme. The quality control element is the distinguishing factor between this type of scheme and the older systems, and the CAA has tried to impress operators with the potential economic benefits of quality management, in addition to the legal needs.

Recording of maintenance work is required by law, so that accident investigation may be carried out. Unfortunately, such investigations have often revealed short-comings in the recording of this work. An operator interested in efficient work planning would, in any case, have to keep a historical database of activities and resources used.

Mandatory inspections and modifications have to be controlled and implemented to comply with post-certification type design standards. The CAA receives all foreign manufacturers' service bulletins (SBs), and reviews the information to decide whether the classification is appropriate for aircraft on the UK register. Complaints have been made about the tendency of non-UK manufacturers to obscure the true classification of SBs for non-technical reasons, such as attempting to avoid legal liability in certain court actions, or just making too many SBs mandatory without regard to the feasibility of implementing them. Obviously, the CAA also classifies all service bulletins issued for UK-designed aircraft.

Legal liability has become a much greater issue with the spread of litigation within the USA and of imitations abroad using the contingency-fee approach. Court investigations will require the production of documents, or at least the interview of persons involved, so that inadequate records will prejudice a verdict.

A modern complication of maintenance certification is the wider use of contracting and leasing. Thus an operator may contract out some of his maintenance work to other organisations, and also lease aircraft to or from other operators who may have AOCs with different levels of authority. Responsible owners of leased aircraft will want to ensure that their assets are being well maintained in order to preserve the book value, but many aircraft are leased on an *ad hoc* basis for terms ranging from months to years in parts of the world far away from their owners. Some accidents have been attributed to incomplete maintenance records leaving the new owners ignorant of the true state of their aircraft.

Analysis of statistics compiled by the CAA for UK accidents and incidents to aircraft above 2,300 kg shows that about 10 per cent have an airworthiness cause, and about 30 per cent have a maintenance involvement. Safety targets for aircraft systems are specified in Joint Aviation Requirement (JAR) 25.1309 for aircraft above 5,700 kg. Overall safety levels at the order of 1 system failure in 10^9 flight hours are now used as the minimum acceptable rate for catastrophic events (those where continued safe flight and landing ceases to be possible). Events of this rarity cannot be demonstrated by experience, a synthetic approach combining component performance variability or failure rate and system connection logic has to be used. This itself is subject to human interpretation.

Structures

Structural inspection is a special part of aircraft maintenance. The main causes of failure are corrosion or fatigue, excess loading is rarely a reason for failure. Corrosion incidence depends on the extent of protective treatment applied in manufacture, and on the subsequent history of the aircraft. Experience has led to improvements in the standard of original protection by manufacturers, and to the use of special corrosion-prevention programmes for imported used aircraft (humid tropical conditions are more severe than the UK climate, especially for problems such as microbiological contamination in fuel tanks).

Modern aircraft structural design is 'fail-safe', rather than 'safe-life', which means that a single failure should be accommodated by alternative load paths. However, it relies on the inspection process detecting the first failure before further damage occurs, and this has not always been achieved. Research into inspection methods and into acceptable levels of crack size and growth are therefore of interest to the CAA. One survey showed that visual inspection has only a 50 per cent chance of detecting a 50 mm crack in a structure, and even a 150 mm crack is not detected on every inspection. Clearly these limitations have to be taken into account when designing aircraft structures and in specifying maintenance schedules. Non-destructive testing (NDT) of various kinds has proved very useful in detecting defects invisible to the human eye, but a successful NDT process for a particular defect usually has to be set up by a trained engineer for use by other staff, and it therefore lacks the intelligent approach of an experienced inspector (NDT is described in a later section).

Aircraft design lives are typically 60,000 flight hours converted into cycles at appropriate average utilisations for the length of flight, so that short-haul designs have higher design cycles than long-haul. Extensions beyond this life may be obtained by mandatory structural inspection audits defined in CAA Airworthiness Notice No 89 (1978), or in similar FAA Notices. This requires the manufacturer to perform a structural integrity audit and produce a Supplementary Structural Inspection Document (SSID).

Recently the FAA has implemented another review of older aircraft, using industry task forces for each manufacturer, following the incident in 1988 when a high-time Aloha Airlines' Boeing 737 lost a large section of upper fuselage (see Case Studies, Chapter 7). Reports on Boeing and McDonnell Douglas older aircraft were published in 1989, others for Lockheed, Airbus and Fokker are to come. These reports specify mandatory work on each type of aircraft, at average costs of around $500,000 each in some cases. Although expensive, these amounts are much less than the sums which some operators are contemplating spending on re-engining to comply with new Stage 3 noise regulations.

JOINT AVIATION REQUIREMENTS

JAR, the Joint Aviation Requirements (was Joint Airworthiness Requirements) is a move to harmonise regulations within Europe for unified design codes of civil aircraft. The eventual aim is to produce a system in common with the USA FAR codes, so that national variations in the certifying of new aircraft will disappear.

Europe, for these purposes, is not the EC 12; JAR involves 13 countries: 8 from the EC, plus the 3 Scandinavian non-EC nations, Austria, and Switzerland. Smaller EC countries without significant aerospace industries are not participants. There are also discussions with the European Conference on Civil Aviation (ECAC), a much wider body of 22 countries which includes all JAR members.

Detailed work on JARs began in the 1970s, starting with the requirements for large transport aircraft (over 5,700 kg). These were first issued as JAR-25 in 1974, which were based on the USA FAA FAR-25 regulations for such aircraft. An agreement followed in 1979 by which some states adopted JAR-25 as the sole code. The first aircraft to be certificated to JAR-25 was the British Aerospace (BAe) 146 in 1983. A memorandum of understanding (MoU) for future airworthiness procedures (FAP) was signed in 1987 by 11 states; the remaining two countries have since signed the MoU.

A European Joint Aviation Authority (JAA) management structure has been established, with an executive board and technical committees. A single European Type Certification team evaluates each aircraft for which an FAP application is made. The first aircraft to undergo this process was the Dornier Do.328 in 1988. This means that the application of requirements is now joint, but the legal endorsement is still national.

At some future date (post-1992?) there will be one authority with sole legal responsibility, operating from a central office through local offices based on the current national authorities under FAP Stage 2. This will resemble the FAA system now used in the USA.

In addition to JAR-25, there are JAR-E for engines (also agreed), JAR-21 for products and parts, JAR-22 for sailplanes, JAR-23 for light aircraft (may become JAR-Commuter), JAR-VLA for very light aircraft, JAR-AWO for all-weather operations, JAR-145 for maintenance organisations with large aircraft. A JAR-helicopter code is not so advanced. Further progress is to be made in the regulation of aircraft maintenance and 'continuing airworthiness'.

Much of the stimulus for this is, of course, the Single European Act scheduled to take effect in 1993. This establishes the free movement within the EC of goods, services, staff and capital. Thus aircraft and parts should be easily movable for sale, lease and operation with no administrative burdens. Maintenance work should be possible in any EC country; technicians, engineers and flight crew must be able to transfer between countries.

There were other reasons for implementing JARs, among them being the realisation that the fragmented national system in Europe was harmful to the European industry itself, hindering development and sales of aircraft. Most aircraft are now international projects, so it makes sense to have common certification. Disagreements between Britain and the USA about certification of aircraft had led to some major changes being requested on certain aircraft types, or even to some types not being imported. These differences have been reduced in recent years; for example, the Boeing 757 required relatively little alteration for UK certification, whereas the Boeing 707 was extensively changed in the UK version.

Another significant problem was the demand for technical expertise in overseeing the regulations. The operation of the airworthiness regulatory system relies heavily on interpretation — the rules alone cannot specify every possible requirement in detail.

Operation of JAR

The JAR system is administered by an organisation, headed by the Directors General, with six members responsible for broad policy, political issues and appeals. Below them is the JAA Committee, composed of members from the Authorities in the participating states. Its function is to decide on major issues. Other Boards, such as those for JAR-25, manufacturers (AECMA), and operators (AEA, ERA), report to it. The JAA Committee also controls the sections which perform the main work — divided into Regulation, Certification, Maintenance, Operation.

The Regulation section has technical study groups to investigate into specific areas. The Certification section has certification teams for each new aircraft type; these also handle the continuing airworthiness of the type. Thus there are teams for new types built and operated in Europe such as the A320, A330, A340, Do.328 etc., and also for aircraft not built in Europe but operated on European registers, such as Boeing 747-400, McDonnell Douglas MD-11, Boeing de Havilland Dash 8. The Maintenance and Operations sections are to be formed later.

Some of the procedures and terminology used by JAA follow that of FAA. Changes to JAR will be first issued as Notice of Proposed Amendment (NPA), like the FAA Notice of Proposed Rule-Making (NPRM). JAA issues Advisory Circulars — Joint (ACJs) in the same fashion as the FAA Advisory Circulars. These address specific problems that have arisen on aircraft. Other publications are the Advisory Material — Joint (AMJ), which explains the requirements and the reasoning behind them.

Cooperation with FAA is maintained by regular meetings between specialists. Notices issued by one side will receive comment from the other, and all FAR amendments will be considered for inclusion into JAR.

Problems with FAR and JAR Reconciliation

Some examples of the difficulties that will have to be faced in producing a complete international JAR are:

Derivative versions of aircraft. This is the interpretation of what is a 'new design' for certification purposes, a recent example being the Boeing 747-400. The upper deck of this aircraft was not constructed to meet improved safety standards which Europeans and the US FAA agreed should apply to all new airliners from 1980. The FAA had agreed with Boeing that 'grandfather rights' protected its original design, but the JAA had told Boeing that this was not acceptable. Boeing apparently forgot about this while delivering the first aircraft in the USA, but encountered objections when making the first European deliveries. The JAA nations gave Boeing up to two years to design the necessary retrofit modifications, and certificated the aircraft temporarily. This was seen as a 'trial of strength' with the FAA, although the FAA did not publicly comment.

Structural testing. The FAA rules require structural strength to be established, not necessarily by testing to destruction in their final form; strength may be proved by calculations and limited component testing. European rules require final-form tests to destruction, and fatigue testing as a separate procedure. FAA rules did not originally require fatigue testing of a complete fuselage specimen, a section being sufficient. Some US manufacturers have gone beyond the minimum FAA requirements but JAA prefers to see the structural testing regulations raised to the European level.

CAA or FAA — Impact on the operator

As an example of the different effects of CAA and FAA registration, consider an airline, based outside the UK and certificated by the CAA, operating US manufactured aircraft. It has to comply with CAA airworthiness directives (ADs) and local ADs. For two aircraft types the numbers applicable to the airframe only are:

Aircraft	Total ADs	FAA only ADs	CAA extra ADs
Boeing 747	237	148	89
Lockheed L1011	177	87	90

The additional ADs from the CAA produce an appreciable amount of extra work for the airline, which faces competition from other operators certificated by the FAA and therefore not required to perform such extra work.

The most notable recent example of this difference was in structural requirements for the Boeing 747-400 upper deck floor strengthening. The European JAA insisting that, as a new design, the aircraft be capable of withstanding the pressure difference resulting from a 20 ft^2 (1.85 m^2) hole in the fuselage, against the original design

Plate 2 Concorde major maintenance at BA Heathrow base

requirement for a 12.5 ft^2 (1.15 m^2) hole. Modifications, to comply with this, increased weight by 250 lb (115 kg) on an aircraft already very weight-sensitive, and cause an estimated extra fuel cost equal to about US \$5500 per year per aircraft.

REGISTRATION, CERTIFICATION AND MAINTENANCE OF AIRCRAFT
(CAP 396 — Feb 1990)

PART ONE — LEGISLATION

The International Civil Aviation Organisation (ICAO)

The Chicago Convention of 1944 set up ICAO, founded in 1947, to promote agreement between nations in aviation. One of the ICAO functions is to promote international standards and recommended practices for air safety; these are written in the Annexes to the Convention. Annexe 8 covers Airworthiness of Aircraft, giving broad standards to be enforced by national authorities.

The United Kingdom is a member of ICAO. The UK national authority for airworthiness is the Civil Aviation Authority (CAA).

The Civil Aviation Act and the Air Navigation Order

The UK air safety legislation is contained in the Civil Aviation Act and described in the Air Navigation Order (ANO) and Regulations — available as CAP 393.

The Civil Aviation Authority (CAA)

This was formed in 1972, to regulate air transport in the UK. It combined the economical and technical functions previously performed by separate bodies.

Airworthiness and operating standards are the responsibility of the CAA Safety Regulation Group (SRG), based at London Gatwick Airport.

Operating standards
Design and manufacturing standards

Licensing standards
Medical
Support services

Aircraft maintenance involves the first three of these divisions, providing aircraft maintenance standards, airworthiness requirements and airworthiness notices, Maintenance engineer licensing, respectively.

British Civil Airworthiness Requirements (BCAR)

These cover the design, production, testing, operation and maintenance of aircraft and equipment. They are published in sections, under various headings. Some BCAR sections have been superseded by European Joint Aviation Requirements (JAR), and more progress in this direction is expected, including requirements for maintenance, as defined earlier in the chapter. The objective is that products certificated in one country using JAR should be validated in another with minimum additional requirements. The intention is to integrate European JAR and United States of America FAR into one code at a future date.

Certificate of Airworthiness (C of A)

An aircraft must have a current C of A in order to fly; this is issued under the law of the country in which the aircraft is registered. The UK C of A becomes invalid if the aircraft is 'repaired, replaced, removed, overhauled, or modified in a manner not approved by the CAA', or 'any inspection, or modification classified as mandatory by the CAA that ensures the aircraft remains airworthy has not been carried out'.

When the C of A is issued, the category of use is also specified. For large civil aircraft this will normally be Transport Category (Passenger) or Transport Category (Cargo); thus a cargo aircraft is not allowed to carry passengers.

The Air Operator's Certificate (AOC)

Aircraft registered in the UK must fly on public transport in accordance with the terms of the Air Operator's Certificate (AOC) granted by the CAA. This signifies that the holder is considered to be 'competent to secure the safe operation' of the specific aircraft detailed on the AOC. For this purpose, the CAA appraises the organisation, staff, training, equipment and maintenance practices of the operator.

Before granting an AOC, the CAA has to be satisfied that the organisation seeking approval is competent to undertake maintenance of the aircraft types operated by it or has made provision for the aircraft to be maintained by another organisation suitably approved by the CAA for such maintenance in accordance with the Approved Maintenance Schedule (AMS). This wording makes it clear that the aircraft registration, operator's certificate, and maintenance schedule are all associated — the AMS is issued to the operator for that aircraft type; if another organisation owning similar aircraft types then maintains it the original registered operator's AMS must be used for that maintenance work. Conditions for AOC are given in CAP 360.

Approved organisations

CAA approval is needed for handling of materials, processes, repair and overhaul, modification, maintenance. After approval, the CAA can make periodic supervisory checks of the organisation to ensure that appropriate procedures are being maintained.

PART TWO — AIRCRAFT AND EQUIPMENT

This covers approval of aircraft (Type Certification), most of this being of interest to the manufacturer. One of the requirements is a maintenance programme established by the Maintenance Review Board.

Items mentioned here which concern an operator are:

Authorised Release Certificate (Form JAA 1). This is an internationally recognised import/export parts release document issued by organisations specifically approved for the purpose. The certificate signifies that the part has been manufactured or overhauled in compliance with the requirements and specifications called for by the aircraft constructor. It is the duty of an operator to verify that all parts received have the appropriate release documents.

Renewal of the Certificate of Airworthiness. The aircraft must have been maintained to an approved schedule. An inspection must be carried out by a qualified person to determine the amount of work needed to ensure the airworthiness of the aircraft. Checks must be made to ensure that it conforms to the Type Certificate Data Sheet and the Flight Manual. Any mandatory modifications and inspections as called for by the CAA must be carried out, including weighing.

PART THREE — MAINTENANCE

In this section, the term 'registered' assumes an intention to fly the aircraft.

Maintenance of aircraft

The Air Navigation Order Article 9 requires that aircraft registered in the UK for a C of A in the Transport or Aerial Work Categories must be maintained to a maintenance schedule approved by the CAA. The maintenance schedule to be used is prescribed in BCAR Section A Chapters A6-2 and A7-5, and BCAR Section B Chapters B6-2 and B7-5. These cover all categories of aircraft, but here we are concerned with large (over 5700 kg MTWA) transport aircraft.

Certificate of maintenance review

Aircraft and their equipment registered in the UK for transport or aerial work must have a valid certificate of maintenance review (CMR) which states the date on which the review was carried out and the date on which the next review is due as specified in the approved maintenance schedule (AMS) or associated approved document.

The certificate records the current maintenance status of the aircraft against the maintenance schedule and any modifications or inspections required by the CAA. The issue of certificates of release to service and all technical log defects, including the rectification or deferment of these defects, are also noted.

The CMR does not have to coincide with any particular maintenance activity, but must 'not exceed' time limits for a review. These are specified in the AMS. The CMR as issued should state the period of validity and include the signature of the person authorised to issue the certificate.

Maintenance statement

When a CMR is issued, an entry must be made in the aircraft technical log detailing when the next scheduled maintenance inspection is due and any out-of-phase inspections required before that time. This entry is the maintenance statement. For aircraft over 2730 kg MTWA, validity of a CMR shall not normally exceed 4 months; a CMR may be issued as frequently as those responsible consider it necessary.

The person authorised to sign the CMR is stated in the AMS or associated approval document. For organisations approved in accordance with BCAR Section A Chapter A8-13 (M1 Organisations), the person or persons authorised to sign a CMR are employed and nominated by the organisation concerned in accordance with A8-13. In other cases the signatory is an engineer with a Type Rated Licence in two categories (other than 'X' — Compasses) appropriate to the type of aircraft.

Certificate of release to service

The ANO 1989 Article 11 requires that an aircraft registered in the UK and issued with a C of A shall not fly without a certificate of release to service (CRS) being issued following:

— Overhauls, repairs, replacements, modifications and mandatory inspections
— Maintenance to the relevant AMS
— Work on radio equipment or survival craft done on the aircraft.

Exceptions to this are possible if the aircraft is at such a place that it is impracticable to repair or replace a part in accordance with the requirements for a CRS being issued. Under those circumstances the commander may fly the aircraft to the nearest facility for the work to be carried out, if it is safe to do so in his opinion. Other exceptions are not discussed here.

The CRS as issued must be signed in all the relevant work categories for the work done. For a set of inspections or tests contained in a check specified in the AMS, a single CRS is sufficient. Those signing must be satisfied that all work has been properly carried out using the correct and up to date manuals, drawings, specifications, recommended tools and test gear, and in a suitable working environment.

A CRS may only be signed by:

— the holder of an aircraft maintenance engineer's licence validated by the CAA,
— a person approved by the CAA as being competent to issue the certificate.

Maintenance organisations approved under BCAR A8 are required to nominate staff as signatories to CRS, CMR, recommendations for C of A, and personal authorisation certificates (PACs).

Personal authorisation certificates are part of the 'Company Approval' scheme of BCAR A8. The certificate details the privileges of the holder for such issues; only the nominated person approved by the CAA may issue personal authorisation certificates. These may only be used in organisations which have the Company Approval from the CAA.

Limited and simple authorisations allow organisations approved under BCAR to issue company authorisation to engineers having a licence without type rating (LWTR) to perform some tasks outside their Licence category. Thus a LWTR holder in Category 'X' (Electrical) could perform a wheel change. These authorisations are normally for line maintenance work and limited in scope; formal on-the-job training is needed.

Modification to aircraft

Modifications are changes to aircraft and their equipment or substitution of parts. The full meaning is defined in BCAR Section A Chapter A2-5, and Section B Chapter B2-5. All modifications affecting airworthiness must be approved by the CAA and must comply with BCAR applicable at the time of original certification. Modifications often involve design changes; aircraft operators possess limited design authority, so the modification is usually devised by the manufacturer.

The UK CAA classes modifications as either minor or major.

Minor modifications regarded by the CAA as relatively unimportant may be designed, embodied and certified by an approved organisation or licensed aircraft maintenance engineer. Minor modifications which are more important require approval by the CAA directly or by an approved design organisation.

Modification approval requires a form detailing the modification, its applicability and relevant drawings or specifications. A Civil Modification Record of work done must be kept; the CAA may inspect this as required.

Major modifications require a more extensive approval process by the CAA, including a Certificate of Design (Modification) and the issue of an airworthiness approval note (AAN) by the CAA. A civil modifications record of these must also be kept.

Mandatory modifications of UK origin

Modifications considered essential to the airworthiness of the aircraft are classed as Mandatory and identified by a CAA Airworthiness Directive (AD) number.

Initial notification of the modification to all operators and maintenance organisations is by a service bulletin (SB) or technical news sheet published by the approved organisation. This is further described in CAP 476. If higher priority is needed, publication by Telex or similar means is used. The CAA then issues an emergency airworthiness directive to all operators of the aircraft type and to CAA Safety Regulation Group Area and Overseas Offices.

Mandatory modifications and inspections of foreign origin

For aircraft of foreign origin, modifications or inspections considered as mandatory by their airworthiness authority are automatically classed as mandatory by the CAA for such aircraft operated in the UK, unless the CAA specifically rules to the contrary. Procedures are summarised in 'Foreign Airworthiness Directives' (CAP 474) and 'Additional Airworthiness Directives' (CAP 473).

Certification of modifications

All modification incorporation work must be supervised either by an approved organisation or by a licensed aircraft maintenance engineer in the appropriate category. Before a certificate of release to service is issued, it should be confirmed that the correct drawings and literature for the modification have been used, and that the modification has been correctly carried out, tested and inspected.

Modification record book

This must be kept and maintained for all UK registered aircraft over 2730 kg MTWA. The owner/operator is responsible for keeping this up to date.

Mandatory reports

An operator or commander of every public transport aircraft registered in the UK who makes, repairs or overhauls an aircraft, or who signs a certificate of maintenance review or of release to service shall make a report to the CAA of any incident, defect, or malfunction to the aircraft or its equipment which would endanger the aircraft or its occupants. Flight data recordings prior to and relevant to the incident must be preserved for at least 14 days after the date on which the report was made to the CAA.

Weight and balance

The aircraft must have regular checks on its weight and centre-of-gravity. Procedures for doing this are described.

PART FOUR — DOCUMENTS FOR AIRCRAFT

Log books

The ANO requires that log books be kept for the aircraft and each engine and propeller if fitted. Use of computer records is now accepted as an alternative to traditional paper documents. Log books must be preserved for two years after the aircraft or engine has been withdrawn from use.

Technical log

Aircraft registered in the UK for transport or aerial work must carry and maintain a technical log. This must be compiled by the operator and be related to the type of aircraft operated and routes flown. Mandatory minimum information required in the technical log is given in BCAR. After every flight, the commander shall enter in the technical log the flight times and any defects known to him. It is acceptable to enter these for the last of a series of flights made by the commander on the same day.

The technical log should contain:

— a valid certificate of maintenance review;
— a maintenance statement;
— a sector record;
— a deferred defect record.

All technical log entries must be in duplicate, one copy to be removed before every flight.

The flight manual

This is mainly the concern of flight crew, however the engineering and maintenance department will have need to refer to it and may contribute to it. The manual sets out the limitations, recommended procedures and information necessary for the safe operation of the aircraft.

Operations manual

This is also required by the ANO, and is intended for use by flight and cabin crew, flight planning staff, flight despatchers and ground engineering staff.

Master minimum equipment list (MMEL)

This is a permissive list of items that may temporarily be inoperative on an aircraft although still maintaining the desired level of safety at the time of despatch on revenue operations whilst operating within a controlled and sound programme of repairs, replacement and servicing.

The MMEL is a list which may be produced by the aircraft manufacturer or by the Airworthiness Authority, and covers all aircraft of a specified type. This is described more fully in CAP 549. In developing a MMEL, due consideration is given to the appropriate air navigation legislation, design requirements, airworthiness authority policy, operational factors and mandatory stipulations applicable to the type, e.g. ADs, ANs and the Flight Manual requirements.

Minimum equipment list (MEL)

MMEL is used by an operator to develop a MEL applicable solely to his own operation.

The MEL must be no less restrictive than the applicable MMEL but may include additional advisory material and define any additional or modified operational procedures.

LICENSING — AIRCRAFT MAINTENANCE ENGINEERS (CAP 468 Section L)

British Civil Airworthiness Requirements (BCARs), of which Section L is a part, are published by the Civil Aviation Authority (CAA). Section L covers the grant, extension and renewal of aircraft maintenance engineers' licences, and the approval and recognition of applicable training. The requirements of Section L also recognise the Standards prescribed by the International Civil Aviation Organisation for the grant and extension of licences.

Licences and categories

Article 12 of the Air Navigation Order (ANO) gives the CAA responsibility for grant, extension and renewal of aircraft maintenance engineers' licences in specified categories.

The CAA will grant a licence 'subject to such conditions as it thinks fit, upon its being satisfied that an applicant is a fit person to hold the licence, and has furnished such evidence and passed such examinations and tests the CAA may require for the purpose of establishing that the applicant has sufficient knowledge, experience, competence and skill in aeronautical engineering.'

Licences are granted and extended within the defined categories given in Table 1.5. Generally, there are two parts to each category:

(a) Licence without type rating (LWTR),
(b) Type ratings.

Licence without type rating: This licence does not in itself confer any certification responsibilities or privileges. It is, however, a prerequisite for the grant of the relevant type ratings which confer the privileges of certification appropriate to that type rating.

CAA approval of organisations under BCAR Section A Chapters A8-13 and A8-18 will normally require an appropriate LWTR to be held before authorisation for maintenance certification may be granted.

There is also a 'workshop licence', equivalent to the LWTR on aircraft, for use by operators with corporate approval schemes.

Table 1.5   CAA licence categories

Categories	LWTR Rating/Sub-divisions	Type Ratings in Accordance with Notice No. 10
'A' — Aeroplanes	Aeroplanes 1 Aeroplanes 2	Paras 5.0, 5.1, 5.5.1, 5.5 Paras 5.6.1, 5.6.2
'B' — Aeroplanes — Rotorcraft	Granted concurrently with a Category 'B' Type Rating only. Requires a relevant Category 'A' Type Rating.	Paras 5.0, 5.1, 5.5.1 and 5.5 (less pressurised types and aircraft over 5700 kg) Paras 7.1, 7.3
'C' — Engines	Piston engines — aeroplanes Turbine engines — aeroplanes	Para 6.3 Paras 6.4, 6.5, 6.6
'A' & 'C' — Rotorcraft	Piston-engined rotorcraft Turbine-engined rotorcraft	Para 7.1 Paras 7.3, 7.4
'A' & 'C' — Airships	Piston-engined airships Turbine-engined airships	Not granted — See Notice No. 10, para 14
'D' — Piston Engines	(Granted concurrently with a Type Rating only)	Para 6.3
'X' — Electrical	Electrical	Para 9
'X' — Instruments	Instruments	Paras 8 and 10
'X' — Automatic Pilots	Automatic pilots — Aeroplanes Automatic pilots — Rotorcraft	Paras 10 and 13 Para 13
'X' — Combined Category	Instruments/automatic pilots	Para 10
'X' — Compass Compensation	Compass compensation and adjustment	Compass compensation and adjustment
'R' — Radio — Radio	Communication and navigation Radar	Para 12.2 Para 12.3

Table 1.6 CAA type ratings, extract

Category	Paragraph of Notice No. 10	Types/Systems Covered
'A' — Aeroplanes 2	5.6.1 5.6.2	Pressurised aeroplanes over 5,700 kg.
'C' — Engines	6.4	Jet-turbine engines of 22.25 kN and below, including APUs.
	6.5	Prop-turbine engines, including APUs.
	6.6	Jet-turbine engines over 22.25 kN and Prop-turbine engines not listed in para 6.5 A.N.10, including APUs.
'B' — Rotorcraft	7.4	Turbine-engined rotorcraft over 2,730 kg
'X' — Instruments	8.1	General aircraft instruments.
	8.4	Flight directors, electrical gyro.
	8.8	Compasses, excluding compensation.
'X' — Electrical	9.4	Constant-frequency AC generators.
'X' — Combined	10.1.1–6	All general instrumentation, FD, autopilot, INS, compasses, GPWS.
'R' — Radio	12.2	Communications and navigation.
	12.3	Primary radar: weather, doppler, etc. Secondary radar: DME, transponders.
'X' — Autopilots	13.3	ILS coupled autopilots.

Type ratings: Type ratings confer on the holder of a licence privileges and certification responsibilities for certain aircraft registered in the UK. The certification responsibilities are described in Airworthiness Notice No. 3.

Type ratings are designated in Notice No. 10; a summary is given here in Table 1.6. Type ratings are not granted for certain aircraft listed in paragraph 14 of Airworthiness Notice No. 10; such aircraft are maintained under procedures covered by BCAR Section A Chapters A8-13 and A8-18. Type ratings are not granted in Category 'B' (under 5700 kg MTWA) for any pressurised aeroplane or aeroplanes over 5700 kg MTWA, or for rotorcraft over 2730 kg MTWA. Type ratings in Category 'D' are not granted for piston engines exceeding 500 kW (670 BHP) power or for any turbine engine.

Validity of licences

Licenses are issued for a maximum period of 5 years. Use of a licence with a type rating to issue certification requires the holder to have been engaged, in the preceding 2 years, for periods totalling at least 6 months, on work affording experience comparable with that required for the grant of the licence.

Application and procedures

Licence without type rating: Application is made to the CAA on Form AD 300. This includes a section for experience gained, for which the applicant must obtain signatures. Documents referring to military service, training, foreign licences, professional qualifications, should be submitted to the CAA in support of the application.

Applicants should have studied the current ANO, BCAR Sections A and L, and airworthiness notices, and make a declaration to this effect. The CAA informs applicants of examination appointments.

Type rating: This will be an extension to the LWTR, which must already be held in the appropriate category. The certification shall normally be made by an engineer who has regular professional contact with the applicant and who has held a UK licence in the same discipline for at least 2 years.

Successful completion by the applicant of a CAA-recognised type training course within the last 3 years may be required.

Grant and extension of licences

Candidates for a licence must be at least 20 years of age (LWTR) or 21 years of age (type rating). They shall be able to read, write and carry out technical discussions in the English language, and be able to provide evidence of suitable experience and training. Extensions are dependent on satisfactory examination standards.

Experience requirements within specified minimum recent periods must be confirmed.

Examination procedures

Examination for licence without type rating is normally in two parts, written and oral.

A type rating requires oral examination on the appropriate subjects, except where satisfactory completion of a CAA-recognised type training course is necessary.

Information on the format of examinations is provided by the CAA. These include multiple-choice question papers, an essay paper, and oral examination where specified. Candidates who fail may re-apply after a minimum interval of 3 months further applicable experience in the category being sought. Conditions are also set out for candidates who fail during a training course.

Licence renewal procedures

Licences are normally renewed on application provided that the holder has been engaged on work of comparable experience for a total of at least 6 months in the 24 months up to the expiry date of the licence. Holders are responsible for ensuring that their licence remains valid. Licences cannot be back-dated.

Licences which have lapsed for less than 2 years may be considered for renewal without examination provided that the holder has obtained suitable experience in 6 of the 24 months up to the date of application. Licences which have lapsed for more than 2 years cannot be renewed without examination of the holder.

Approval/recognition of training organisations or courses

This details the requirements for training organisations seeking approval of courses giving basic aircraft engineering training and preparing students for CAA examinations in LWTR categories, and for recognition of type training courses.

Courses may be approved for mechanical or avionic trades as specified in CAP 468. The organisation, staff, their experience and numbers, classrooms, workshops, equipment, technical library and attendance records must be approved or made available for inspection by the CAA. Detailed syllabuses must be submitted for approval. Any material changes in staff, syllabuses or facilities made after the initial submission must be notified to the CAA to ensure continuance of approval or recognition.

Examination syllabus

The examinations are based on a number of modules, the contents of each being detailed in Appendix 1 of CAP 468. Each module contains subject headings, and each subject is divided into levels corresponding to LWTR and type rating. The three levels cover:

— general principles and familiarisation;

— comprehension of principles and salient features with a practical ability to assess operational conditions;

— detailed knowledge of all aspects of the subject (not always required).

In applying these levels of knowledge to subjects relating to aircraft, engines, systems, and items of equipment, aspects taken into account should be:

— theoretical principles;
— constructional arrangements, functional and design features;
— maintenance practices;
— normal, deteriorated and failed conditions.

Comments

It can be seen that a thorough training is required for aircraft maintenance workers. The licence without type rating takes from 3 to 4 years to acquire from start, and there may be further qualifications beyond this. A typical operator will not send candidates for type rating until they have LWTR in two categories, such as engine/airframe on the same aircraft type, or electrical/instrument categories. Suitable candidates are tradesmen seeking higher responsibility and promotion, whom the employer regards as having a good prospect of success in the examinations. Although extensive knowledge of the aircraft or system is required, the CAA now tends to place more emphasis on understanding of the subject, since a practising engineer will refer to maintenance manuals for factual information.

The extent of training means that operators intending to expand their business or to acquire new aircraft types must plan far ahead. It also means that engineers studying

Plate 3 Servicing at Monarch Airlines, Luton (courtesy of Monarch Airlines)

and working towards a licence need reassurance that the effort will be worthwhile, and that employers must act to retain these acquired skills. This applies not only to the legal aspects, but also to the practical needs of the person. There is a tendency in large production organisations to let staff over-specialise, so that qualified engineers may only see a small part of the whole aircraft servicing or maintenance task and forget or lose interest in the rest. A further problem is that the regular advent of new aircraft types requires retraining of the workforce, and not everyone likes a life of new learning.

ENGINEERING SUPPORT (CAP 360)

Requirements for engineering support necessary for the grant of an Air Operator's Certificate (AOC) by the UK Civil Aviation Authority (CAA) are set out in the document CAP 360 Part Two, published by the CAA.

Part One of CAP 360 describes the issue and variation of Air Operator's Certificates, and the requirements for the operation of aircraft. This is mainly concerned with aircraft flying operations, loading, aircrew training and organisation.

CAP 360 Part Two applies to all AOC operators. Items covered in the document include:

— administration;
— maintenance support arrangements;
— contracting-out maintenance;
— airworthiness control procedures;
— maintenance facilities;
— quality control and assurance;
— the Engineering Manual;
— the Technical Log.

Initial application for the grant of an AOC is made to the CAA, who are responsible for investigating the proposed engineering support arrangements. If accepted, the operator must inform the CAA of subsequent changes which may affect the engineering support arrangements, such as the type of aircraft operated.

The operator must satisfy the CAA that the engineering support organisation is to a satisfactory standard. By this is meant the personnel, accommodation, equipment and facilities, organisation, procedures and documentation provided for engineering support of the aircraft. The organisation must correspond to the category of maintenance approval sought, whether corporate approval schemes suitable for larger aircraft and operators, or licensed engineer schemes. Licence qualifications of staff should obviously cover the aircraft types to be operated.

The CAA also requires that the engineering support organisation should have management systems designed to ensure overall control of the continuing airworthiness of the operator's aircraft fleet. This includes the quality control and assurance necessary to achieve satisfactory standards of continuing airworthiness, compliance with mandatory modifications and inspections, and efficient work planning and progress.

For maintenance organisations using the corporate approval scheme, CAP 360 lays great stress on the management of quality control and assurance in the organisation. The operator's management system must be shown to be capable of organising and controlling the work on aircraft. The issue of company authorisations to staff is explained carefully, including personal responsibility, scope of authorisation, and conditions of issue. Personnel authorised under the terms of an approval granted in accordance with this scheme should normally be directly employed by that organisation. CAP 360 states conditions for authorisation of personnel employed by other organisations who contract work for the AOC holder.

Quality control and assurance (Q&A) requirements for organisations using an approval scheme for aircraft maintenance are stated. These cover terms of reference and responsibility for Q&A staff, records of staff and their qualifications, planning of regular quality checks, formal reporting of findings by these checks and follow-up action of recommendations made.

For other kinds of maintenance organisation, the requirements of a management system to exercise quality control and ensure efficient work planning and progress are given.

The organisation must satisfy the CAA that it has sufficient qualified staff for the work to be done. This may be provided by internal training or by contract from another source. Training for management, supervisory and inspection staff who are to be responsible for engineering support should be provided. Numbers of staff trained before introduction of a new aircraft type should take into account the complexity of the type, the size of fleet and nature of operations. Training of mechanics and use of refresher courses and other training is also specified. Records should be kept of courses taken and results achieved in examinations.

Contracting

The arrangements and procedures to be followed when an operator contracts engineering support to another organisation are specified. These contractors must be acceptable to CAA. Appropriate conditions for these arrangements are laid down. A formal maintenance agreement should be drawn up indicating the division of airworthiness responsibilities for both parties. Topics covered should include provision of maintenance equipment, technical information, completion of records, supply and storage of spares, notification and correction of defects, mandatory modifications and quality surveillance, etc. A person must be nominated by the operator for engineering liaison purposes, and should visit the contractor regularly to ensure that the agreed standards are being maintained.

Maintenance support may only be contracted to a foreign organisation if it is appropriately approved by the CAA or by the responsible authority of the organisation.

Organisation

The operator must provide a description of his maintenance support arrangements for the direction and guidance of flight crew and maintenance personnel engaged in the day to day operation and maintenance support of his aircraft. This manual is also required as a basis for CAA acceptance of the arrangements.

The operator may publish a separate Engineering Manual or use a section of the Operations Manual devoted to these requirements, or refer to the Exposition of the Approved Maintenance Organisation. The Exposition should be divided between base and line maintenance, and may be further sub-divided for ease of use. The Manual should take account of other CAA publications related to aircraft operation and maintenance.

Procedures for the regular review of maintenance schedules after experience must exist, to ensure feedback. An airworthiness occurrence control and reporting system must be in use to provide continuous analysis, notification of events, and continuing airworthiness of the aircraft. Responsibility for co-ordination of this activity and any follow-up action should be assigned to a suitably qualified senior official in the organisation. An engineering member of the organisation should be appointed to deal with technical aspects of these occurrences. The operational and maintenance responsibilities may be held by one person if the company role and organisation structure reflect this.

A system of assessment should be in operation to provide a continuous analysis of the operator's control systems in use. The system should cover significant incidents and defects, repetitive incidents and defects, deferred and carried forward defects, unscheduled removals and system performance. Manufacturers responsible for type certification of the aircraft should also receive reports of occurrences to that type, so that they may issue service instructions to all operators.

Mandatory occurrence reporting in accordance with the Air Navigation Order is described in a separate publication, CAP 382, for aircraft exceeding 2300 kg MTWA. The CAA mandatory occurrence reporting (MOR) scheme was devised to inform the CAA of hazardous or potentially hazardous incidents and defects, to disseminate knowledge of these occurrences so that others may learn from them, and to enable safety assessment of each occurrence so that necessary action may be taken.

Methods for monitoring and reporting where sub-contractors are used in maintenance are also specified. Procedures for receiving and responding to manufacturer's service bulletins and similar technical publications must also be demonstrated.

The organisation should have a department responsible for technical records and a data recording system. Items to be recorded include:

— hours or cycles used in maintenance schedule control
— calendar time for maintenance schedule control
— logs for major components such as engines
— component changes, inspections and modification work done.

The technical records department should also be responsible for accuracy of documents issued for maintenance checks. Working documents such as lists of inspections, component changes, modifications, test procedures, outstanding and carried forward defects should be available. All worksheets or job cards should be identifiable by an issue number and associated clearly with the relevant part approved maintenance schedule. Missing worksheets or cards should be apparent so that completion of all work is ensured. The entire work package for a particular check should be identified for that aircraft check and operator by a covering control sheet.

Technical records must be retained for two years after disposal of the aircraft, engine or components. Only records necessary to prove all requirements have been met for issuance of release to service need to be retained. Computer storage and analysis may be used in a technical records system by agreement with the CAA. Requirements for this in terms of integrity and accuracy are given.

The technical library must hold and make available to personnel concerned, the necessary technical data, such as CAA publications, the ANO, manufacturer's manuals, any relevant service information, any other related literature appropriate to the aircraft types covered by the AOC and copies of appropriate company manuals, procedures and instructions. A person must be appointed to be responsible for the technical library. Arrangements must be made for the notice and supply of amendments, storage and correct issue of drawings, and for manuals or service information to be made available to line maintenance stations and kept up to date. Microfilm or computer recording of maintenance manuals should also comply with these requirements.

Technical logs are required for each aircraft operated. Particulars to be recorded in these are described more fully in BCAR, Section A. The technical records department retrieves, analyses and stores copies of the aircraft technical log for reference.

Stores for aircraft materials and parts should consist of quarantine and bonded stores; these requirements are more fully described in civil aircraft airworthiness inspection procedures (CAAIP). Control of shelf life, provisioning, requisition and tool stores should be provided.

Accommodation

Accommodation should be provided to house all aircraft during planned maintenance checks. The importance of providing adequate hangar facilities, not only at the main base where scheduled work is normally done, but also at other bases, is stressed for tasks which involve dismantling with consequent risk of contamination. Heating, lighting, and cleanliness are also significant. Office accommodation for quality control, inspection and supervision staff must be satisfactory for their work, such as use of manuals and drawings.

The equipment used for aircraft maintenance should correspond to that specified in the maintenance manual.

Access equipment such as stands, hoists, platforms or docks must be available and capable of reaching all parts of the aircraft. Racking or similar stowage for removed panels, control surfaces, components, etc. should be provided. Workshops for the repair or servicing of components taken off the aircraft must be separate from the aircraft maintenance hangar and equipped for the work to be done in respect of tools, equipment, special test equipment and documentation. Separation of areas used for stripping and cleaning, recharging, dismantling, assembling and testing is recommended to avoid contamination.

Practical operation

An example of the company approval scheme in use is given for a UK operator of aircraft types which may only be maintained under the company approval scheme. The maintenance workers have basic training to license without type rating standard (LWTR) and type training to the level required for signing a certificate of release to service (CRS).

Monitoring of the work is done by an internal quality assurance group, on a planned frequency. The objective is to see that the system is capable of meeting the requirements of a CAA-approved aircraft maintenance organisation. This involves checking the equipment, tools, documents, procedures, and other resources. The aircraft work must also be audited by this quality assurance.

The CAA sampling inspection also exists to verify that an organisation is operating correctly. Recommendations and actions follow automatically from the authority to quality assurance department, but it is still necessary to have review meetings.

Allowable deferred defects (ADD) are entered in a special log (this is CAA requirement) and should be reviewed and if possible cleared within a company-specified target time. Minimum equipment list (MEL) determination is regarded as a matter principally for flight operations department with engineering input. Engineering has responsibility for ensuring that aircraft are kept to MEL standard.

AIRCRAFT NOISE

The noise limits for most civil jet transports are defined by the regulations in ICAO Annex 16 Chapter 2 and also in FAA FAR Part 36 Stage 2. This is commonly referred to as 'Chapter 2/Stage 2'. Most of the regulations are identical; ICAO Annex 16 is the international version, and FAR Part 36 is the US version. These came into force for the USA on 1 January 1985. This led to the banning of noisier pre-Chapter 2 aircraft from most industrialised countries of North America and Europe, though operations in many less developed countries continued. Such aircraft had higher fuel consumption than their successors, hence the phasing out did not meet with great objections from operators.

A further reduction in noise levels, the 'Chapter 3/Stage 3' standard, has been defined but proposed dates for worldwide introduction are still being discussed. There is a considerable number of Stage 2 aircraft in service, and operators were not prevented from buying them after the announcement of Stage 3 regulations. Aircraft that do not meet Chapter 3/Stage 3 requirements include Boeing 727s, most Boeing 737s, McDonnell Douglas DC-9s, some older Boeing 747s, British Aerospace BAC 1-11s with hush kits, Fokker F28s. Aircraft that are acceptable include the Boeing 757s and Boeing 767s, most Boeing 747s, McDonnell Douglas DC-10s, McDonnell Douglas MD-80s, Lockheed L1011 TriStars, British Aerospace BAe 146s, Airbus A300s, Airbus A310s.

Proposals are now being made for introducing Chapter 3/Stage 3 requirements. The European Civil Aviation Conference (ECAC), which is a trade body of 22 member airlines, recommended that no more non-Chapter 2 aircraft be added to members' registers after 1 October 1990, and that from March 1995 an operating ban be applied to all non-Chapter 3 aircraft as they reach 25 years of age. Parts of this recommendation are likely to become EC law. A final ban on operating such aircraft would take effect in the year 2015. Some member countries have already announced their own schemes. For instance, the five Nordic countries intend to ban all non-Chapter 3 aircraft from the year 2000. The US Industry Task Force on Airport and Capacity Improvement suggested 1 December 1990 as the start date for the 'no addition' rule, with a phasing out over 15 years from 1994. Other countries favour later dates for the introduction of Stage 3 and longer retention of the older Stage 2 aircraft. ICAO was to discuss proposals before 1990 and produce a draft recommendation, but the ICAO 27th assembly in 1989 did not reach an agreement. In the USA some local authorities, faced with pressure from local airport residents, have imposed their own bans on

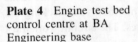

Plate 4 Engine test bed control centre at BA Engineering base

non-Stage 3 aircraft. In Britain the BAA has introduced surcharges on landing fees for the noisier types.

The cost of implementing the ECAC proposals is estimated to be $4,000 million or more in premature retirement of otherwise usable aircraft. If re-engining or fitting hush kits is allowed, a much higher cost is estimated, though the aircraft would then be usable. An ICAO study gives estimates ranging from $0.5 billion, for a mix of modified aircraft and replacements at the latest date, up to $6 billion for total replacement of all noisy aircraft at the earliest date.

Aircraft manufacturers have obviously concentrated on sales of new aircraft, but engine manufacturers will also consider modifications. These can be 'hush kits' fitted to existing engines, reducing the fan and exhaust noise, or replacement of the complete

Plate 5 Engine control system checks

engine with a modern Stage 3 version. Schemes for re-engining Boeing 727s with Pratt & Whitney JT8D-217s (3 fitted) or GE/SNECMA CFM-56s (2 fitted), BAC 1-11s and Fokker F28s with Rolls-Royce Tays, were announced by independent companies, mostly in the USA.

Hush kits increase the weight, drag and fuel consumption of the aircraft, so there is a continuing cost penalty after the initial cost of fitting is paid. Installation is estimated to cost from $1.5 million to $3 million for the widely-used Pratt & Whitney JT8D turbofan engine; this is a significant proportion of the airframe value for older Boeing 727s. Some operators are using the opportunity to have other improvements fitted to the aircraft, such as cockpit electronics upgrades, to regain some of the economic losses of the hush kits. Of course, the most important benefit of the hush kit is the ability to continue flying into Stage 3 restricted airports.

CHAPTER 2 AIRLINE ECONOMICS AND MAINTENANCE COSTS

AIRLLINE ECONOMICS AND THE AIRCRAFT

The fundamental cost relation for passenger-carrying flights is the cost per seat-km, expressed as a function of route length. The graph in Fig. 2.1 shows results from US airlines in 1988, for many aircraft types, so it is an 'envelope' curve. This is the consequence of several factors:

1 Payload — Range. All aircraft must operate within maximum weight limits, imposed for reasons of structural strength, fatigue life and aircraft performance. In addition, most aircraft have a limited fuel tank capacity. Fig. 2.2 defines an aircraft which has a payload-capacity limit below its structural zero-fuel weight limit. In other words, it is not possible to fill the cabin and holds with a load that exceeds the worst case expected in an emergency landing, when the aircraft might have to jettison fuel for safety reasons. The load with passengers only is less than that with passengers and freight; airlines use this difference to increase revenue from freight on shorter flights, where fuel is not critical.

As the desired range increases and more fuel is needed, a point is reached where payload has to be removed to keep the total aircraft weight within safe limits. This is the segment marked 'maximum take-off weight limit'. When the fuel limit at full tanks is reached, range can only be increased by reducing the fuel burn rate with a lower aircraft weight, lowering the payload at an even greater rate. This is of little practical use in airline operations.

2 Block speed. This is the average speed from departure to arrival at airport terminal stands, corresponding to the published timetable. The aircraft can only fly at its cruise speed for part of the flight, and for shorter flights this is a smaller segment because of unavoidable delays in taxying, take-off, climb and descent. The result is that average speed only approaches maximum cruise on long flights. Fig. 2.3 shows data from US airlines in 1988, for many aircraft types.

3 Aircraft output. The combination of these gives the aircraft production measured in capacity tonne-km per hour (CTK/hr), Fig. 2.4.

Thus each aircraft type has its best range for maximum productivity. Airlines will try to obtain and use the aircraft most suited to their route network.

Analysis of the actual seat capacities and route lengths used by US operators of large aircraft (over 100 seats) in the year 1988—9 is shown in Fig. 2.5. (Compare this with brochure values.) This shows three main groups of aircraft:

— the long range — over 4000 km, with 200 to 400 seats
— the medium range — 1500 to 3000 km, with 170 to 300 seats
— the short range — 500 to 1000 km, with 100 to 150 seats.

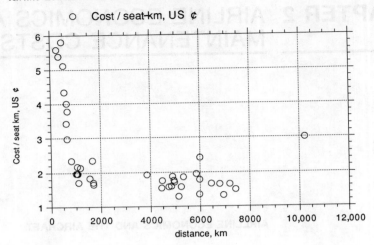

Fig. 2.1 Civil aircraft direct operating costs by range

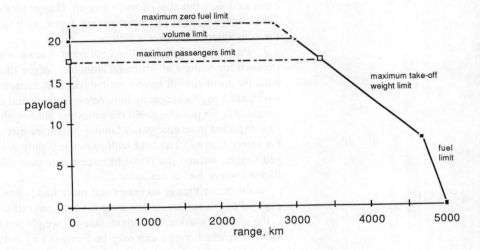

Fig. 2.2 Example payload-range diagram

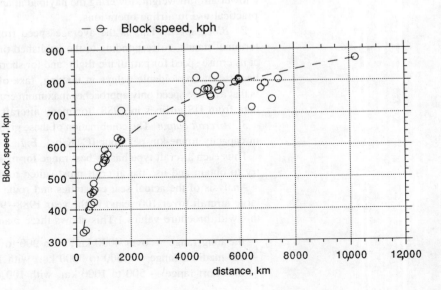

Fig. 2.3 Block speeds of civil aircraft by range

Fig. 2.4 Productivity of a civil aircraft by range

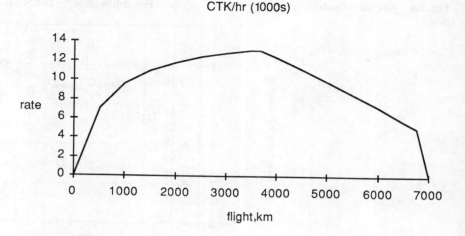

Fig. 2.5 Seats and ranges of civil aircraft in use

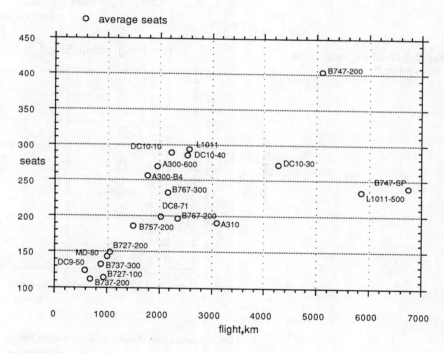

Smaller aircraft (under 100 seats) used on even shorter flights (below 500 km) are not shown here. These are the 'commuter' aircraft, mostly with turboprop engines.

4 Costs. This is further affected by the actual aircraft utilisation which can be achieved, and by the division of aircraft costs between those which remain fixed in relation to flying rate and those which vary directly with flying.

Aircraft utilisation is governed by such factors as the ratio of aircraft loading and unloading time on the ground to flying time (greater for short-range aircraft), the public demand for flights through the day or night, local airport restrictions on night flying, and the spread of seasonal demand through the year. The consequence is that regular flying at the peak rate is not possible with most operations (some very long-haul operators with extensive routes can approach this maximum). This is shown in Fig. 2.6, for US airline data in 1988−9 of various jet aircraft types.

Fig. 2.6 Aircraft utilisation by range

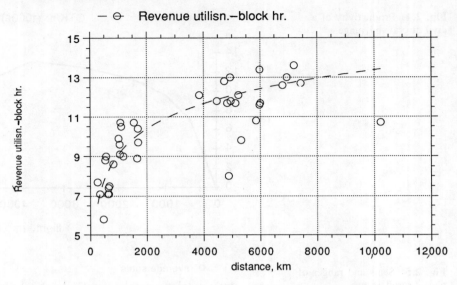

Fig. 2.7 Fuel consumption of civil aircraft by range

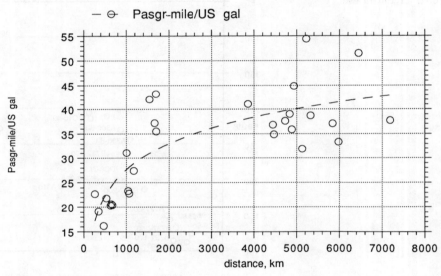

5 Fuel consumption. Another factor which has an adverse effect on the economics of short-haul air transport is the fuel consumption rate. The greater proportion of trip time spent in climb and descent, plus the lower cruise altitudes when flying short distances, cause a higher fuel burn per passenger-km than in long-haul operations, even though many of these short-range aircraft have turboprop engines with low fuel consumption. Results from US airline data for 1988 in 'automobile' units are shown in Fig. 2.7 as passenger-miles per gallon, which therefore includes the load-factor effects of unused seats. Note that 1 Imperial gallon equals 1.2 US gallons.

PRINCIPLES OF AIRLINE ECONOMICS

Airline production

Airline production is usually measured in seat-kilometres, the result of multiplying the seats offered for sale on each flight by the distance flown. Usually this is referred to as the 'available seat-km' (ASK), or sometimes 'capacity seat-km'. Airline costs are often based on this unit of output, so the standard cost measure used in many airline reports and aircraft sales brochures is the US cent (¢) per seat-km.

It is rarely possible for an airline to sell all the seats it offers, so another measure of airline output is the revenue passenger-kilometre (RPK), often used as a base for comparing airline incomes.

Load factor

Another statistic frequently used in the industry is the passenger load factor, which is the ratio of passenger-km to seat-km. A value of about 60 per cent for this used to be regarded as typical for profitable operations in scheduled services, but the growing use of yield management techniques with computer reservation systems has raised the average load factor expected by scheduled service airlines to around 70 per cent. These operate to timetables published in advance, and higher load factors may mean that passengers are being turned away or even over-booked. Charter airlines which operate group booking organised by tour operators expect to achieve higher load factors, over 80 per cent. Passengers are induced to travel at times convenient for the airline, by being offered lower fares than for a scheduled flight over the same route.

Direct operating costs (DOC)

Costs are usually divided into 'direct' and 'indirect'. This breakdown is traditional in the industry. Direct costs in airline terms are those which can be identified as being related to the aircraft. These are in turn split into 'fixed' (depreciation, interest, insurance) and 'variable' (crew, fuel, maintenance, navigation and landing charges). The indirect costs are those related to the airline itself, such as stations, sales and advertising, administration, passenger services. A very crude rule is that the direct to indirect ratio is 50 : 50, but this is influenced by the type of market in which the airline operates. Lower-cost airlines must have lower indirect charges; carriers operating in well-developed markets have high marketing costs.

Aircraft manufacturers concentrate on the direct costs when selling to airlines as customers. These will obviously depend on the aircraft type, its size, range, fuel consumption and spares needs. They will also depend on factors within the airline's control, such as crew salaries, maintenance policies and, above all, on the aircraft utilisation expected. Utilisation is measured in flying hours per year or per day; average values of 4000 hr per year or 12 hr per day are regarded as good for long-haul intercontinental operations. Aircraft depreciation is normally made over the economic life of the equipment, which is now about 15 to 20 years. A high annual utilisation will result in low hourly charges for depreciation and make it easier to earn profits or to cut fares. Many airlines do not actually own their aircraft, but lease them. Either method has a fixed annual capital charge.

Flight operations

This category includes crew, fuel, landing and en-route costs. These functions traditionally fall under the heading of aircraft operations, which used to be managed by a senior pilot. It is now common to combine these with Engineering and Maintenance in one Technical Department for management purposes, but the cost categories are retained.

Crew costs include the salaries of pilots and the cost of their training. New aircraft purchases lead to a higher than normal training element, so it is common to spread this over several years, treating it as amortisation of a capital asset. Crew costs are affected by pilot utilisation. This depends on legal limits to prevent crews being tired, and on labour agreements negotiated between the airline and pilots' unions. Some airlines pay strictly by the time flown, others pay a fixed salary and allow pilots to bid for routes in order of seniority; this usually means that the more experienced pilots get higher expense allowances.

Fuel costs are now a very high proportion of an aircraft's direct operating cost, usually up to 40 per cent. This is higher for older, less fuel-efficient types and lower for the newer more fuel-efficient types. One method of minimising fuel consumption is to use careful flight planning and operation. These functions are now increasingly being managed by computers and automatic control systems on the aircraft. These may be supervised by the pilot in such a way that he has the final authority on the course flown by the aircraft.

Landing and en route costs include charges levied by airports, as well as air traffic control.

Aircraft maintenance and overhaul

To ensure safety, airlines must keep their aircraft in good condition. A maintenance scheme is negotiated with the local government air-safety regulating body, based on recommendations made by the aircraft manufacturer and the experience of the airlines and regulatory authorities. This covers everything from routine servicing before every take-off to major overhauls done every few years.

Procedures for fitting modifications devised by the manufacturer and demanded by the authorities are also laid down. Such modifications may occur as a result of experience by other users of the aircraft or as a result of accidents to the aircraft. Many other modifications are produced by manufacturers as product improvement, and it is up to the airline to decide whether to fit them.

Maintenance costs range from 10 per cent to 20 per cent of the total aircraft operating cost. Newer aircraft have lower costs than older ones because they have not reached the major overhaul age yet. Aircraft maintenance requires heavy investment in hangars, workshops and other equipment. Small airlines may therefore contract their maintenance to larger airlines or to specialist overhaul organisations.

Another method of reducing the aircraft support costs is for a group of airlines using the same type of aircraft to arrange a work-sharing scheme, so that one partner handles the engines, another the airframes, another the components, and so on. Examples of this are KSSU (KLM, SAS, Swissair, UTA) and ATLAS (Air France, Alitalia, Lufthansa, Sabena) in Europe.

Maintenance costs can be reduced by continuous monitoring of the aircraft condition, so that unnecessary work is avoided, or by incentive contracting to encourage profit-sharing with a supplier.

Aircraft financing

In recent years, many different ways of providing airlines with the means to buy or use new aircraft have been devised. These have been the result of international competition in aircraft sales, poor airline profitability in the recessions of the 1970s and 1980s, and the immense burden of financing the ever-growing fleets.

Leasing has become popular because of tax advantages to the airline, however some governments have acted to reduce this in order to retain taxes. One way round the problem has been the growth of intermediate leasing companies based in tax-advantaged regions, who pass on the benefit to airlines in lower rates. Another reason for leasing is to overcome foreign-exchange limits imposed by governments or bodies such as the International Monetary Fund (IMF) on developing countries.

A form of lease which has become very popular is the 'leveraged lease'. With this the leasing company becomes the owner of the asset, although providing only part of the capital for it, often 20 per cent to 40 per cent. The rest is borrowed as a loan whose interest rate depends on the credit-ranking of the lease company. By being the owner, the lease company obtains full tax benefit. Some of the aircraft orders placed by this method have been very large; an example is the purchase for Delta Airlines of $600 million worth of Boeing 737s.

Another form of lease is the operating lease, which originally was intended to fill short-term gaps in an airline's capacity. There are two main types: 'dry' in which only the aircraft is leased, and 'wet' in which a completely crewed and serviced aircraft is leased to an airline. This lease does not have the tax advantages of long-term contracts, but some recently negotiated ones have options to buy or terminate after a few years, so that they have the flexibility of short-term leases with the advantages of long-term ones. An example is British Airways' order for $700 million of Boeing 737s; this was done to provide the airline with new aircraft without incurring capital costs prior to its sale by the British Government.

A form of lease developed to meet the needs of the developing countries is the cross-border lease. Here the countries of manufacture, registration, operation and finance may all be different. An example was the supply of aircraft to Mozambique Airlines, registered in France and operated under UK laws, and ultimately financed by US banks based in Britain.

A full finance lease is one where the leasing company provides all the funds; this is popular with Japanese banks, perhaps as a way of dealing with trade surpluses built up in some countries. Examples are orders from Thai Airways and Cathay Pacific.

COST OF AIRCRAFT MAINTENANCE

Aircraft maintenance costs are expected to depend on the type of aircraft (age, technology, role) and the kind of operation for which the aircraft is used (short-haul, long-haul).

Aircraft operating costs

To illustrate these effects for civil aircraft, consider the results reported for US operators as quoted in quarterly statistics published in magazines such as *Aviation Week and Space Technology*, or *Air Transport World*. These statistics were a requirement of the US CAB route licensing procedure before deregulation, but their use has continued longer than envisaged by the Deregulation Act of 1978 and they are still filed with the US Department of Transportation Office of Aviation Information Management. The costs shown in this chapter are all 'direct' — that is, only items which can be attributed to a particular type of aircraft are given, such as crew, fuel, depreciation or rental (referred to as 'write-off') and maintenance. Direct maintenance cost represents work done on the aircraft or its components (maintenance burden is an overhead allowance to reflect allocated charges for the fleet in technical support, facilities, etc.).

Airline costs such as ticketing, sales, administration, and so on, which depend more on routes and marketing policies, are excluded. The costs are given per block hour (time between airport terminal gates) and thus depend partly on the aircraft utilisation (average daily flying hours) — higher utilisation will spread the overheads over more flying hours.

Wide-body aircraft costs

Two aircraft types in wide use by the airline industry are shown: the Boeing 747, which first entered service in 1970, and the Boeing 767, which first entered service in 1982. The 747 is the main long-haul airliner in use world-wide; the 767 is a medium-haul successor to the original Boeing 707 jet airliner. The 747 was therefore designed before the fuel price increases of the 1970s, and the 767 was designed when prices were at a peak.

Table 2.1 *Boeing 747 costs of four major US operators in year 1986 (Northwest, Pan American, Trans World and United Airlines; average number of aircraft in use = 121)*

(US $ per block hour)	$	%
Crew	787	17%
Fuel	2,030	44%
Depreciation & rental	672	14%
Total maintenance	1,117	24%
(Other items)	36	1%
Total aircraft cost	$4,642	100%

Table 2.2 *Boeing 747 costs by reporting period in year 1986*

Quarter (US $ per block hour)	1st	2nd	3rd	4th	Year total
Crew	779	762	772	836	787
Fuel	2,770	2,014	1,698	1,725	2,030
Depreciation & rental	561	596	606	929	672
Total maintenance	1,167	1,040	1,027	1,251	1,117
(Other items)	35	25	37	50	36
Total aircraft cost	$5,312	$4,437	$4,140	$4,791	$4,642

Fig. 2.8 Boeing 747 costs by category for all operators

Boeing 747 costs in 1986—US $ per block hour

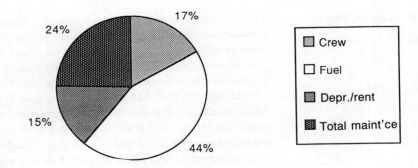

Fig. 2.9 Boeing 747 costs by period for all operators

Boeing 747 costs in 1986—US $ per block hour

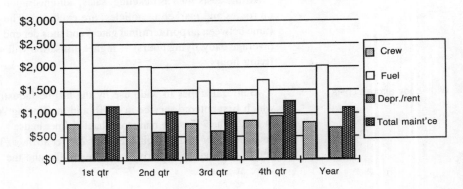

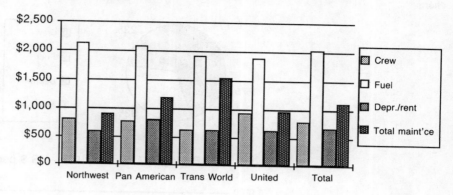

Fig. 2.10 Boeing 747 costs by operator for year

Table 2.3   *Boeing 767 costs of four major operators in year 1986 (American, Delta, Trans World, United Airlines; average number of aircraft in use = 62)*

(US $ per block hour)	$	%
Crew	504	23%
Fuel	720	32%
Depreciation & rental	596	27%
Total maintenance	377	17%
(Other items)	31	1%
Total aircraft cost	$2,228	100%

Table 2.4   *Boeing 767 costs by period in the year 1986*

Quarter (US $ per block hour)	1st	2nd	3rd	4th	Year total
Crew	545	508	496	473	504
Fuel	1,021	720	600	589	720
Depreciation & rental	733	633	525	517	596
Total maintenance	419	348	336	412	377
(Other items)	30	28	30	34	31
Total aircraft cost	$2,748	$2,237	$1,987	$2,025	$2,228

Looking at the results for the calendar year 1986, it is seen from Tables 2.1−2.4 and Figs 2.8−2.11 that:

Total hourly maintenance costs were 25 per cent of the Boeing 747 aircraft cost and 17 per cent of the Boeing 767 aircraft cost. This would be expected, with the 747 being much older than the 767 and therefore requiring more major maintenance. However, it should also be noted that the share belonging to depreciation is much lower with the 747 — it represents historic cost unadjusted for inflation.

Fuel costs dominate the other categories for the 747; fuel represents the largest single cost item for the older aircraft types. For the 767, fuel cost is only slightly greater than that for the other categories.

Fig. 2.11 Boeing 767 costs charts

Boeing 767 block hour costs in 1986

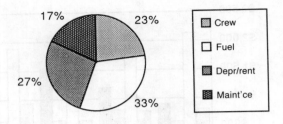

Boeing 767 costs in 1986—US $ per block hour

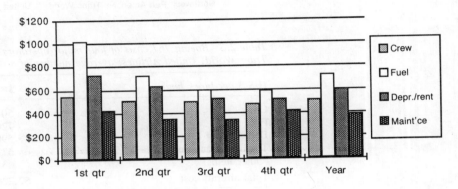

Boeing 767 costs in 1986—US $ per block hour

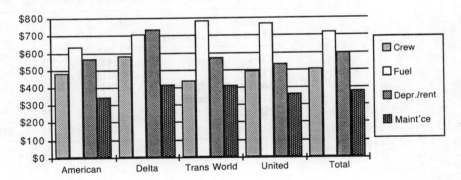

There are wide differences in the reported costs for the same category between operators. Some of these are due to accounting policy, some result from differences in the average ages of fleets used by these operators and some may be due to differences in operations flown by the airlines.

Fuel prices declined sharply during the year 1986, apparently by 40 per cent. The 1990 Middle East crisis produced very high peak prices, followed by a decline.

If it is assumed that fuel and aircraft prices are the same for all operators in the industry, then the two other expense categories which can be influenced by airline managements are the crew and maintenance costs. In a competitive market where fares and revenue rates are similar for all operators, the airline which makes the most efficient use of these two resources will also show the best return on investment.

Narrow-body aircraft costs

We will look next at more recently published results for some narrow-body airliners in widespread use, also for the US airline industry, averaged across all operators in the USA. The Boeing 727-200 is the oldest design, dating from the 1960s; the Boeing 757 and McDonnell Douglas MD-80 are more recent designs or derivatives, entering service in the 1980s.

Expressing the results in unit costs, US cents per seat-km, allows more meaningful

Fig. 2.12 Narrow-body aircraft costs by aircraft type

Boeing 757-200 operating costs in 1988

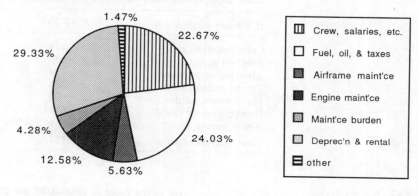

Boeing 727-200 operating costs in 1988

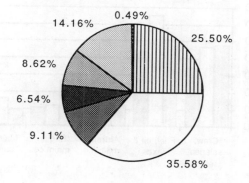
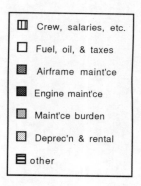

McDonnell-Douglas MD-80 costs in 1988

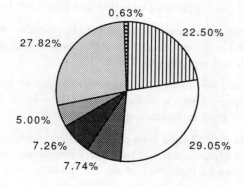
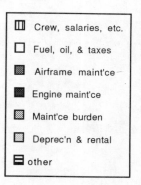

Table 2.5 Narrow-body aircraft cost shares by category

(US $ per block hour)	B757-200	B727-200	MD-80
Crew, salaries, etc.	23%	25%	22%
Fuel, oil & taxes	24%	36%	29%
Airframe maintenance	6%	9%	8%
Engine maintenance	13%	7%	7%
Maintenance burden	4%	9%	5%
Depreciation & rentals	29%	14%	28%

Table 2.6 Narrow-body aircraft DOC summary

(US $ per block hour)	B757-200	B727-200	MD-80
Crew, salaries, etc.	479	466	346
Fuel, oil & taxes	507	651	447
Airframe maintenance	119	167	119
Engine maintenance	266	120	112
Maintenance burden	90	158	77
Depreciation & rental	619	259	428
(Other items)	31	8	10
Total aircraft expense	$2,111	$1,829	$1,539

Fig. 2.13 Narrow-body aircraft costs by category

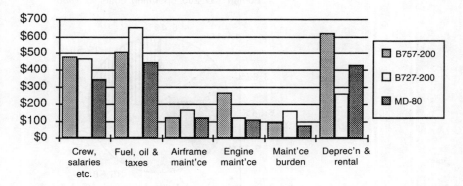

US airline costs in 1988—US$ per block hour

comparison with the revenue fare per seat-km that the operator must charge to make a profit. From the earlier discussion of airline economics, it is obvious that short-haul fares per km must be higher than long-haul. From these figures, it is seen that:

> Total maintenance costs (direct plus burden) range from 20 per cent to 25 per cent of the total aircraft direct cost, with the higher figure again being for the older aircraft type (Boeing 727-200).

> The lower fuel cost of the newer-technology Boeing 757 is somewhat offset by higher engine maintenance costs. (These B-757 figures include both Rolls-Royce and Pratt & Whitney engined aircraft.)

> Boeing 757 crew costs per seat-km are much less than for Boeing 727, owing to the higher number of passengers carried and the two-pilot crew possible on the advanced flight deck of the 757 aircraft.

Table 2.7 Narrow-body aircraft costs per unit of output

Cost/seat-km, US ¢	B757-200	B727-200	MD-80
Crew	0.66	0.90	0.71
Fuel	0.70	1.25	0.92
Airframe maintenance	0.17	0.32	0.25
Engine maintenance	0.37	0.23	0.23
Maintenance burden	0.13	0.30	0.16
Depreciation & rental	0.86	0.50	0.88
Total aircraft expense	2.89	3.50	3.15

Fig. 2.14 Narrow-body unit costs by category

US airline industry DOC, ¢ per seat-km

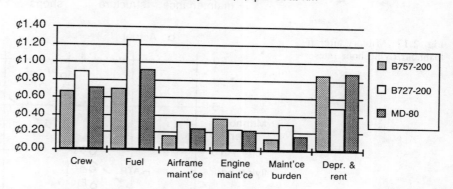

Fig. 2.15 Civil aircraft manhour/flying hour rates

US airline maintenance manhrs /flying hr

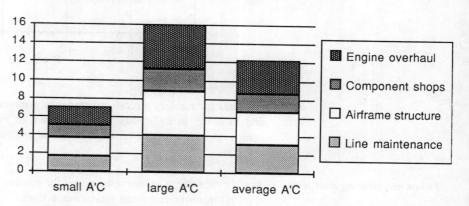

Twenty years of technological progress in civil aircraft between 1960 and 1980 produced a much smaller improvement in unit costs per seat-km than the preceding 20 years from 1940 to 1960, even when adjusted for inflation.

Maintenance manhours

A measure of maintenance cost often used by operators is the ratio of maintenance manhours to aircraft flying hours. This is useful for first estimates in budgeting, and is also used as a target in military aircraft procurement contracts. Cost figures expressed in money are affected by inflation and exchange rate fluctuations, whereas manhour figures are not subject to these influences. Manhours can, however, be influenced by training, experience, and technological changes.

Values for US Airlines, from Airclaims, published in *Aviation Week* (24 July 1989), are shown in Figs 2.14 and 2.15.

Fig. 2.16 Civil aircraft manhour/flying hour breakdown

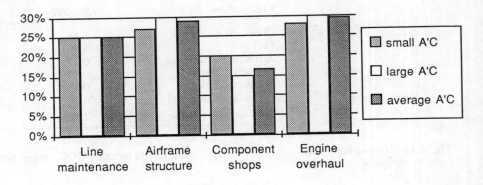

US airline maintenance manhrs / flying hr

Fig. 2.17 Military aircraft manhour/flying hour rates

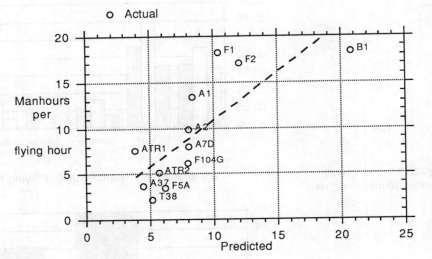

Values for military aircraft maintenance manhours/flying hours (from Serghides and Fielding, in *Reliability '87*) are shown in Fig. 2.17. The actual results are compared with a prediction from statistical analysis of the data.

Airline engineering staff levels

Another measure of maintenance cost is the number or proportion of an airline's staff engaged in engineering and maintenance work.

The figures in Figs 2.18 and 2.19 are from the IATA Report for 1989. Looking at results for the top 24 carriers, measured by total employees, it is seen that maintenance and overhaul employees were typically from 14 per cent to 24 per cent of the total, with some notable exceptions. A plot shows an approximately linear relation over a wide range of airline sizes, with the possible exception of a few very large carriers. The average for all 24 carriers was 18 per cent of employees in maintenance and overhaul. These 24 carriers represent 68 per cent of the total IATA membership employees in that year; for all IATA members maintenance and overhaul employees were 19 per cent of the total. Not all major world airlines are IATA members; in 1989 IATA output represented 73 per cent of the international tonne-km as reported to ICAO (excluding Aeroflot).

Also shown in Fig. 2.19 are trends over the five years 1985−1989 for three groups

Fig. 2.18 IATA members,
M&O employees 1989 vs total
M&O employees

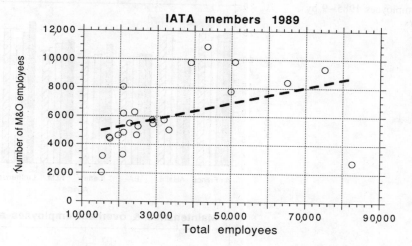

of major airlines: European, United States, and Others. The European airlines show about 20 per cent to 25 per cent of total employees in maintenance and overhaul, with a slight reducing trend. Most of the United States airlines show less than 15 per cent of total employees in maintenance and overhaul, with one notable exception (Eastern Airlines). This may be partly due to higher US wages and also due to economies of scale, since most US airlines are large. Only Swissair, in the European

Table 2.8 IATA members 1989, maintenance and overhaul staff

IATA members in 1989 (ranked by total employees)	Maint. & o'haul employees	Total employees	% M&O
Federal Express	2,756	82,611	3%
American Airlines	9,361	75,086	12%
United Airlines	8,420	65,099	13%
British Airways	9,847	50,959	19%
USAir	7,767	49,948	16%
Lufthansa	10,890	43,565	25%
Air France	9,773	39,111	25%
TWA	5,044	33,299	15%
Continental Airlines	5,746	32,011	18%
Iberia	5,466	29,001	19%
Pan American	5,755	28,784	20%
KLM	5,285	25,000	21%
VARIG	4,674	24,638	19%
Saudi Arabian Airlines	6,271	24,064	26%
Alitalia	5,492	22,719	24%
Japan Air Lines	4,843	21,142	23%
Air Canada	6,182	21,022	29%
Swissair	3,300	20,917	16%
Indian Airlines	8,055	20,905	39%
Pakistan International	4,643	19,691	24%
Qantas Airways	4,400	17,481	25%
Air-India	4,479	17,293	26%
Eastern Air Lines	3,191	15,468	21%
Canadian Airlines International	2,045	15,262	13%
Total	143,685	795,076	

Fig. 2.19 IATA members, M&O employees 1985–9 by operators

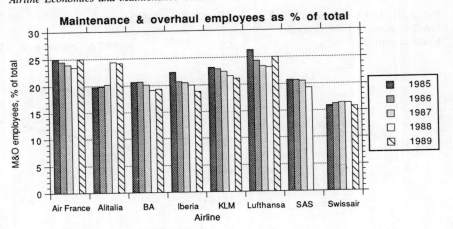

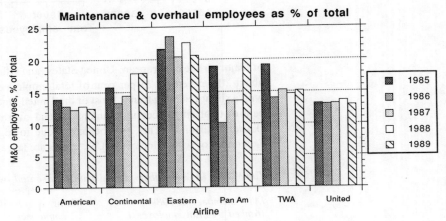

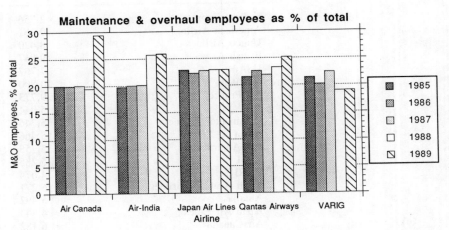

group, approaches US levels for the proportion of employees in engineering and maintenance, despite the high wages of some other EC airlines. What effect the European Single Market deregulation will have on these levels after 1992 remains to be seen. The third group of airlines shows similar shares of staff in engineering and maintenance to the European group, although they operate in very different domestic economies.

Table 2.9 British Airways operating expenses for years 1986—90 (from notes on annual accounts)

Airline operations	Years 1986—90
Staff costs	25%
Depreciation	7%
Aircraft operating leases	3%
Fuel and oil	13%
Engineering & other aircraft costs	6%
Landing fees & en route charges	8%
Handling, catering & other costs	11%
Selling costs	13%
Accommodation & other	14%
Total airline	100%

Fig. 2.20 British Airways expense summary

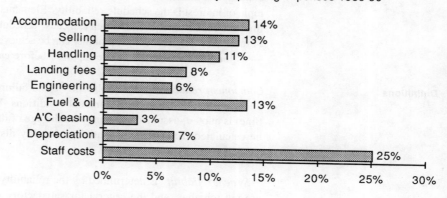

British Airways operating expenses 1986-90

Maintenance and overhaul is thus still a significant part of most airlines' activity, despite the growth of staff in other areas of the airlines and the increasing reliance on independent aircraft-maintenance organisations.

Engineering as an expense

As a perspective on the share of the total airline operating expense taken by engineering, consider the figures reported by one airline. These show that engineering is a lower cost category than selling, for instance. Note that some of the staff costs shown separately here are included in the maintenance costs quoted in the preceding section.

Although aircraft are expensive, airlines are not 'capital intensive'. The largest single cost category is for staff.

CHAPTER 3 SCHEDULES AND CONSTRAINTS

AIRCRAFT RELIABILITY

Introduction

This section explains the terms and procedures used by engineers working in commercial aircraft reliability. This differs from other reliability work because the topic of interest is the schedule reliability. Elements include aircraft readiness, down time and repair time, events which can cause schedule interruptions such as diversions or turnbacks. High schedule reliability can be achieved with unreliable aircraft systems — as long as the aircraft can be repaired before each flight without causing delay.

Definitions

Component reliability is the probability of no failure over a specified period of time under particular use and environment conditions. When the failure rate (λ per unit time) is quoted, assumed constant with the age of the component, the reliability may be calculated from the exponential probability distribution.

$$R(t) = \exp(-\lambda t) \tag{1}$$

System reliability is determined by the reliability of its components, the way they are put together, and the criteria for satisfactory operation.

Unreliability is the complement of reliability, that is

$$Q(t) = 1 - R(t) \tag{2}$$

Because of the high reliability of modern aircraft, it is often more convenient to discuss unreliability, and measure it as a failure rate, than to quote reliability, thus '1 in 10^8 failure risk' is more easily assimilated than '0.99999999 reliability'. For the constant failure rate assumption

$$Q(t) = 1 - R(t) = 1 - \exp(-\lambda t) \approx \lambda t \tag{3}$$

This approximation, which is intuitively represented as 'failure risk equals failure rate multiplied by duration of risk', is good enough for engineering purposes when λt is less than 10^{-3}, approximately.

Not all component failures cause system failure, and some component unscheduled removals are later found not to be failures. Several reliability measures may be defined. Aircraft reliability, commonly referred to as schedule reliability, includes only those failures that result in a schedule interruption

$$R_{\text{air}} = 1 - \frac{\text{schedule interruptions}}{\text{total revenue departures}} \tag{4}$$

Where R_{air} is the probability of starting and completing a scheduled revenue flight without interruption.

Example

Sample component removal data from a hypothetical aircraft show how to use the definitions to calculate reliability estimates. The component is an avionic item for which 2 per aircraft are fitted. The data covers a period of 100,000 flight hours and 80,000 departures.

total removals (including 20 scheduled)	100
unscheduled removals (failed or suspect)	80
failures (inoperative or below specification)	50
inoperative and caused system failure	26
caused schedule interruption	4

Some important conclusions are immediately obvious. There were $80 - 50 = 30$ unjustified removals — items wrongly removed or later found to be adequate. The sample mean time between failures (MTBF) is $200,000 / 50 = 4,000$ hours. The sample mean time between unscheduled removals (MTBUR) is $200,000 / 80 = 2,500$ hours. The ratio of these measures is sometimes called the 'maintenance efficiency', MTBUR/MTBF, equal to 63 per cent here. (Values around 50 per cent have been persistent over the years for electronic equipment, despite progress in reliability and diagnostics.)

These calculations are based on a sample of field data (actual experience). The comparison with original predictions might have been a failure rate of 33 items per 100,000 hours, corresponding to MTBF of about 3,000 hours, based on a simple rule using parts-counts and standard failure-rate data for a target equipment failure rate of 40 per 100,000 hours. The demonstrated failure rate is apparently within specification, but it should be remembered that since this is a statistical phenomenon, a confidence level should be applied in a real test.

The estimated reliability of this equipment for a 2 hour flight, assuming a failure rate constant with age, is:

$$R(t) = \exp(-\lambda t) = R(t) = \exp(-25 \times 10^{-5} \times 2) = 0.9995$$

The approximate probability of failure is:

$$Q(t) \approx \lambda t = (25 \times 10^{-5} \times 2) = 5 \times 10^{-4}$$

The assumption of constant failure rate, although often made to simplify calculations, is also justified by considerations of the equipment and its maintenance — the sample contains items of various ages, and the equipment itself consists of many different parts.

The choice of mission time is important for reliability estimates. In aircraft operation, it is usual to make this equal to the flight time because all equipment has to be operational at the start of a flight and there is no opportunity to perform repair during the flight. Many components operate on a once-per-flight task. Components which may not always be used, and whose functions cannot be easily checked outside a maintenance base, should have longer mission times, depending on their inspection intervals.

The reliability of a system comprising two of these items can be estimated if it is assumed that the system fails if either item fails and that failures are statistically independent (no common-cause failures). This is equivalent to a 'series system', and its reliability is:

$$R_{system} = R_1 \times R_2$$

It is easier to quote the unreliability:

$$Q_{system} \approx Q_1 + Q_2 = 5 \times 10^{-4} + 5 \times 10^{-4} = 1 \times 10^{-3}$$

If, instead, it is assumed that the system fails only if both items fail, again with independence, this corresponds to a 'parallel system' with:

$$Q_{\text{system}} = Q_1 \times Q_2 = 5 \times 10^{-4} \times 5 \times 10^{-4} = 0.25 \times 10^{-6}$$

Terminology

Despatch reliability is the probability of departing on time, calculated as

$$R = 1 - \frac{\text{delays} + \text{cancellations}}{\text{total departures}}$$

Delays are departures which are late by more than a specified time (often 5 minutes, sometimes 15 minutes).

En route reliability is the probability of completing a flight plan without a deviation, calculated as

$$R = 1 - \frac{\text{air turnbacks} + \text{ground turnbacks} + \text{diversions}}{\text{total departures}}$$

A ground turnback is defined as occurring before take-off; an *air turnback* as occurring after take-off.

Inflight reliability is the same as for en route reliability but excluding ground turnbacks.

The schedule reliability is the probability of starting and completing a scheduled revenue flight without a schedule interruption.

$$R = 1 - \frac{\text{schedule interruptions}}{\text{total departures}}$$

Schedule interruptions include delays, cancellations, turnbacks, diversions.

Schedule reliability combines component and system reliability, maintainability and deferability (the ability to defer maintenance of a non-critical item), and the maintenance efficiency of the organisation performing repairs. Schedule reliability is usually a specified requirement in contracts or sales brochures.

Once in flight, the pilot in command has three alternatives if a failure occurs: continue to the original destination, divert to an alternate destination, or turn back. The first does not affect en route and inflight reliability.

Despatch reliability can be affected if maintenance action is not finished at departure time.

Other reliability measures

Although aircraft reliability can be specified and measured exactly using the foregoing terms, it is not always useful in guiding management action towards identifying problems. Other measures frequently used are:

— Pilot reports of technical defects;
— Engineers' reports of technical defects;
— Average level of deferred defects carried;
— Average time to clear deferred defects;
— Time off service for repairs;
— Usage of standby aircraft or slack time in the schedule;
— Maintenance manhours per flying hour;
— Maintenance cost per flying hour.

Of the measures described, airline operators usually attach great importance to schedule reliability, since this most closely corresponds to the performance offered to the travelling public, namely a promise to convey the passenger in accordance with the published timetable. Pilot reports per flight or flying hour are often used internally by company management as an indication of potential troubles. The actual figures will be affected by crew rostering policy, since pilots are bound to notify defects when they complete a duty on the aircraft. If this happens after every flight, the incidence of reports will be high. Monitoring of the deferred-defect rate and clearance is required by airworthiness authorities.

Attempts to measure aircraft reliability by time out of service for unscheduled repairs are made difficult by the effects of aircraft utilisation. If the aircraft is scheduled for an intensive flying rate, as is often the case with new types, a comparatively small amount of down time will cause aircraft shortages and schedule interruptions. If the aircraft is not scheduled intensively, more time is available for maintenance and staff may react by giving completion a lower priority than for other aircraft types.

Maintenance manhours per flying hour are measured for long-term trends and for planning purposes. Maintenance costs are monitored for budgetary purposes as part of the accounting system. Some components and systems on new aircraft have specific contract targets set for these costs whilst under warranty. Component unscheduled removal rates are measured by reliability programmes in many airlines. Confirmed-defect rates or the complement 'no-fault found'-rates are used as a measure of maintenance diagnostic accuracy by many operators.

THE MAINTENANCE SCHEDULE AND ITS DETERMINATION

The principle behind the construction of modern aircraft-maintenance schedules is the document produced by 'Air Transport Association (ATA) Maintenance Steering Group — 3 Task Force' (MSG-3) in 1980.

Plate 6 Boeing 747 examination of the rear fuselage

History of Maintenance Steering Group (MSG)

The history of this committee and its documents can be traced back to the Federal Aviation Administration (FAA) / Industry Reliability Program of the 1960s. The original programme was aimed at exploiting the new-found increase in propulsion-system reliability consequent on the change from piston to turbine power for civil aircraft. It was recognised that widespread use of 'hard-time' component lives was an ineffective and expensive means of ensuring aircraft safety, but that if these were removed then an alternative scheme was necessary.

The MSG approach

MSG-1 was produced in 1968 and was used to develop the Boeing 747 scheduled maintenance requirements. MSG-2 followed in 1970, and was used with the Lockheed L1011 and McDonnell Douglas DC-10 maintenance programmes. The Association of European Airlines developed EMSG in 1972, as an improvement on MSG-2; it was used for the Airbus A300 and Concorde maintenance schedules. Finally, a joint team collaborated on the development of MSG-3, which was used by the US industry for the Boeing 757 and 767 aircraft maintenance programmes, and is now the current version.

MSG-3

The MSG approach lays down a set of logical rules to be followed in deciding the maintenance policy for an aircraft and its systems. These rules are based on the importance of the component or system, the nature of anticipated failures which may occur in them, the visibility of such faults, and the possible corrective actions. It is not possible to have a set of rules which specify every requirement in advance, because some decisions in the process involve engineering judgement by experienced staff.

In the original MSG-1 and MSG-2 there was considerable scope for interpretation of the rules, which could lead to different results, depending on the experience fed in. One of the objectives of MSG-3 was to tighten, as far as possible, the definitions used by airline engineers and manufacturers so as to leave little room for ambiguity in subsequent discussions.

Implementation

The initial work of implementing the MSG process is divided into several groups such as structures, systems, powerplant, electrical/avionics, flight control/hydraulics, and zonal inspections. Representatives of the operators (launch customers), manufacturers, and regulators comprise the working groups, who are supervised by a steering committee.

The steering committee defines 'specifics' to direct the groups; these include a 'procedures guide' which describes the nature and frequency of aircraft inspections to be used. The forms used by groups and the level of detail to be considered in evaluating maintenance tasks are also defined. The time schedule for the completed report is also specified, since this interacts with the certification and delivery for new aircraft.

The MRB Report

The final report is termed the Maintenance Review Board (MRB) Report. This is produced by the manufacturer and forms the base document from which operators then work. Before this can happen, the MRB document must be approved by the relevant government authority (FAA, CAA, etc.); this may be done in stages. Once this is available, the operator writes his own schedule from the MRB Report, giving the Approved Maintenance Schedule (AMS) as the legal document enforced by the regulatory authority.

The MRB Report also covers operation of the aircraft and some economic considerations in maintenance decisions, these being a function of the operator. The levels of importance for maintenance decisions are (1) technical factors, (2) operational factors, such as length of haul, departure punctuality, spares support, (3) economic factors, such as make/buy, in-house/contract repair. Once produced, the AMS provides the operator's staff with planning information for the necessary materials, labour, and facilities.

Older methods

Before the MSG logic, up to the 1950s and early 1960s, all aircraft maintenance was based on the theory of preventive replacement or restoration, commonly referred to in the industry as 'hard-time'. Fixed lives for all parts or tasks were written into the maintenance schedule and adhered to when planning the work. Extension of these lives to reduce operating costs was obtained by designating selected high-time items for strip and examination by airline engineers in conjunction with airworthiness authority representatives. If this proved satisfactory, then an increase in approved life was granted.

Advantages claimed for this procedure was that it was conservative; most components started with low approved lives and their reliability had to be established by trial in service. Monitoring of the performance and condition of components was provided by the many routine overhauls and some special strip reports. Production planning was easy because of the high frequency of routine replacements.

Disadvantages were the high wastage of usable life for good components in the early stages of service life; unless strong efforts were made to keep the trial units ahead of the remaining population, items would be called off that could have lasted longer. If one of the designated trial units failed before strip examination, another had to be selected. This high rate of removal also made economical spares provisioning difficult to achieve; it could lead to over-provisioning for the mature years which formed the major part of an aircraft's service with the operator. It was also observed with many components that overhaul costs tended to rise with approved life, to meet the demand to 'build in the reliability', so that the actual hourly operating cost did not fall much. Component lives had to be aligned with aircraft check intervals at which the scheduled work was done; any increase in one of these required either a corresponding increase in the other or a revision of the work package in a check.

The most serious disadvantage of this frequent preventive maintenance, however, was the revelation that it did not actually improve the reliability of aircraft components and systems. This discovery did not come about immediately, of course. When the amount of scheduled work was relatively high, the odd few unscheduled removals went unnoticed. Once the approved life had been raised, the unscheduled removal rate of components became dominant and was seen to be unaffected by alteration of the approved life in many cases. Special studies and statistical analyses of aircraft, after checks, revealed what many line staff had claimed, that an aircraft was often more likely to develop faults just after a major check than at other times. The disturbance of complex systems and components for access, test, or changes was likely to introduce errors in adjustment, leaks and contamination of fluids, unsealed connections, and similar nuisance faults.

Much time and effort was also wasted in planning for the removal, at checks, of components which then failed between the plan date and the check visit. Since there was no individual recording of component ages with this system, the only way to guarantee the fitment of a new item at each check was to replace whatever item was already installed, even if it was only a few hours old. In this way unreliable components had very little chance of reaching their nominal approved life.

In the era of piston-engined aircraft, with their lower capital costs and expected flying utilisation, this inefficiency did not matter too much. When jet aircraft of much higher cost, and the utilisation levels needed to absorb this, entered service the cost of this maintenance system rapidly became unbearable to operators.

MSG-1 introduced overhaul or on-condition alternatives in place of the exclusive reliance on hard-time lifing of aircraft components used previously. MSG-1 required engineering judgement used in maintenance-programme development to be quantified and took account of the redundancy designed into newer aircraft types. Quantification was still rather rudimentary, however; usually being the assignment of a rating to selected aspects of the failure risk, consequence, and maintenance action.

MSG-2 included, for the first time, the condition-monitored concept, in addition to the existing two methods of MSG-1. MSG-3 was the result of a task force formed to review MSG-2 experience. Among the reasons cited for doing this were:

— a great increase in fuel prices, with consequent change in cost emphasis
— new types of aircraft with more use of electronics in control and display
— new fatigue design rules requiring damage-tolerance ratings for the structure
— publication of the reliability centred maintenance (RCM) report by the US Government.

Reliability centred maintenance (RCM)

RCM was the result of much practical and theoretical investigation within United Airlines, written up as a contract research report. It was considered to be an improvement over MSG-2 for developing maintenance programmes, because it tackled many of the deficiencies in MSG-2. These were:

— no explicit treatment of fuel conservation
— structural programme logic needed improvement
— change of approach from piece part level to system failure level
— inadequate rules for identifying maintenance significant items (MSIs) and structural significant items (SSIs)
— inadequate and confusing treatment of hidden-function failures
— inadequate rules for defining functions and functional failures
— no treatment of multiple failures
— no treatment of zonal and general inspections
— no discussion of task intervals
— task development needed to be made more rigorous
— no guide for making decisions in the absence of information
— clearer distinction needed between economics and safety/hidden function logic paths
— condition monitoring needed redefinition or elimination
— servicing and lubrication programmes not treated
— system logic needed improvement.

RCM update

RCM itself has been revised and is used by military operators as a basis for maintenance programmes. The current RCM approach is based on the airline/manufacturer maintenance-planning document MSG-3.

The US Department of Defense (DoD) is adapting the RCM analysis approach to developing maintenance plans for new systems. To accomplish this, RCM has been made an inherent part of the MIL-STD-1338-2A logistics support analysis (LSA) system. This new system includes the capability of using either an MSG-2 or an MSG-3 approach. In the DoD method of operation, development of the maintenance plan is an inherent part of the LSA process. The RCM analysis (part of LSA) and the structural integrity program (SIP) result from the core of the maintenance plan. This core data is then supplemented by repair level analysis (RLA) results and other technical and logistics data to completely define maintenance plans for new systems.

MSG-3 in practice

The MSG-3 document is in several sections. Each section was designed to be a separate entity capable of being used independently of the other MSG-3 sections.

MSG-3 uses two different logic diagrams for analysis purposes; one is used for systems and powerplant items, and the other for structures analysis. Both logic sets are a change from previous logic and require thorough understanding before use.

The structures logic diagram was derived from the guidelines given in FAR 25.571 for damage-tolerant fatigue design and makes provision for appendices to be added by the manufacturer that show how he intends to comply with the MSG-3 logic for structures.

The systems and powerplant diagram was developed using the 15 points mentioned above. All these were catered for in MSG-3, to varying extents.

The improvements provided in MSG-3 are:

Maintenance significant items (MSI)

For systems and powerplants an MSI is defined as one that:

— could affect safety, either on the ground or in flight, and/or
— is undetectable during operations, and/or
— could have significant operational economic impact, and/or
— could have significant non-operational economic impact.

Top-down approach

The MSG-3 steering committee considered the use of a 'top-down' approach essential in developing the new logic, as indicated by the change in emphasis from piece-part to system approach.

The systems and powerplant analysis uses this top-down approach, in which the functional failure of a system is considered in relation to other systems. If it can be shown that the functional failure of a specific system has no effect on the operating safety of an aircraft, or will not have a substantial economic impact, then it can be stated that the system is not maintenance significant and therefore requires no routine maintenance activity.

If the functional failure of the system does affect operating safety or cause a substantial economic penalty, it can be classed as maintenance significant and must therefore contain items that require further consideration.

This technique was a complete reversal of the older MSG-2 logic, whereby analysis began with individual components and worked upwards to system level. Thus, where an MSG-2 analysis might have asked 'what happens if No. 2 hydraulic pump fails' and then proceeded to consider the effect on system performance, MSG-3 logic would require the asking of 'what is an unacceptable level of hydraulic-system pressure', and what happens if pressure falls to this point. Use of this method was expected to avoid much unnecessary detailed analysis of small parts, even down to seals, fasteners and such.

System logic

MSG-3 improved on MSG-2 by a complete redesign of the systems and powerplant logic diagram, to guide the user through the decision process and resolve the deficiencies of MSG-2. The logic is in two levels:

Level 1. This determines the consequence of a functional failure. Four questions are asked; depending on the answers, the user is guided into level 2 and one of the 5 task selection categories.

Hidden or evident failure. The first question in level 1 asks: 'Is the occurrence of a functional failure evident to the operating crew during the performance of normal duties?' The answer to this question establishes the nature of functional failure.

Evident safety effect. If the answer to question 1 is 'yes', the user is then directed to the next question which asks: 'Does the functional failure or secondary damage resulting from the functional failure have a direct adverse effect on operating safety?' A 'yes' answer to this question indicates that the functional failure is safety-related and directs the user to the Evident, Safety Effect category of level 2.

Evident economic effect. A 'no' answer to the above question directs the user to the question: 'Does the functional failure have a direct adverse effect on operating capability?' This question is aimed at economic effects, and a 'yes' answer indicates that the functional failure must be considered under the economic, operational effects category. A 'no' answer means that the functional failure should then be analysed under the economic, non-operational effects category.

Hidden failure. If the first question gave a 'no' answer then the functional failure is hidden from the operating crew. This leads to the question: 'Does the combination of a hidden functional failure and one additional failure of a system-related or back-up function have an adverse effect on operating safety?'

Hidden safety effect. A 'yes' answer to this guides the user into the hidden, safety effects category.

Hidden non-safety. A 'no' answer directs the user into the hidden function, non-safety economic effects category of level 2.

It should be noted that all the questions in level 1 are asked of the item's functional failure, but the questions in level 2 are asked of the functional failure's cause.

Level 2. This provides the means to make a task selection which addresses the cause of the functional failure. As stated before, depending on how the questions in level 1 are answered, the user is guided into one of 5 effect categories in level 2.

The 5 effect categories in level 2 are:

— evident functional failure, safety effects;
— evident functional failure, operational economic effects;
— evident functional failure, non-operational economic effects;
— hidden functional failure, safety effects;
— hidden functional failure, non-safety economic effects.

Throughout the diagram, default logic is used. In addition, when level 2 is entered, applicable and effective criteria have to be met.

New definitions in MSG-3

The original 15 points included a request to reconsider whether the term 'condition monitored' should be retained. It was decided to make MSG-3 a task-oriented concept. Therefore the terms condition monitored (CM), hard time (HT) and on-condition (OC) were eliminated and replaced with the specific tasks found in level 2. (But see UK CAA CAP 418, 1978, where these terms are still used.)

The possible task selections found in level 2 are:

— lubrication/servicing;
— operating crew monitoring;
— operational check;
— inspection/functional check;
— restoration;
— discard.

In Safety-related categories — a possible combination of the above.

Fig. 3.1 Simplified MSG-3 logic diagram

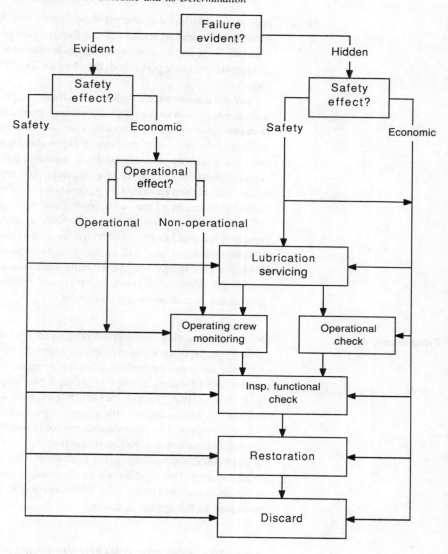

Applicable and effective criteria: Whichever question is asked in level 2, the user must always consider whether the task in question is applicable and effective. To assist the user, the applicability and effectiveness criteria are detailed for each task selection question and its effect category.

The maintenance schedule

The MRB report is the starting point for an airline to prepare its own maintenance schedule. To this may be added tasks generated by:

— manufacturer's maintenance planning document (MPD);
— the airline's engineering department;
— any extra certification and maintenance requirements from CAA, FAA.

The MPD may contain tasks additional to the MRB Report which are recommended, not mandatory. These may be opinions about special techniques developed by or with the manufacturer, or work on non-airworthiness items such as passenger cabin appearance. Airline engineering departments may have company policy for some items that are common across different fleets, which have to be put into the maintenance schedule. Type certification of the aircraft is often conditional on certain special checks and inspections being performed, therefore the locally approved schedule must contain these tasks.

Once the maintenance schedule is finalised, the plans to implement it begin. These include production of all other supporting documents related to the schedule, such as maintenance manuals and training manuals. Discussions about the make-up of work packages take place with production engineering staff, model work cards for every task are made up and stored in a master database (usually on a computer). Arrangements for the supply of consumable and replaceable spare parts have to be made. Training and recruiting programmes for certified trades needed have to be made, based on estimates of the skills needed and workload expected.

If the aircraft is a significant addition to the existing fleets in numbers or size, then hangar space will have to be obtained for it. It is also very likely that special access equipment and test gear will be required. Ground servicing equipment will have to be obtained for hangar use and for ramp turnround use. Many of these facilities have lead times measured in years, and there are relatively few manufacturers of some specialised aircraft servicing equipment.

Experience of MSG-3

MSG-3 looks a very bureaucratic process to an outsider. It requires a large amount of analysis, experience and time to implement. In its favour is the discipline it imposes on users' thinking, the precise definition it requires, and the early review of potential problems it provides. Because of these, it has been accepted worldwide as a sound method of deriving aircraft maintenance programmes. Versions of it are even used in countries which otherwise try to avoid dependence on western industrial technology.

Examples quoted by one manufacturer for the workload involved in applying MSG-3 for the first time are 4,500 staff manhours in working group meetings, thousands of pages used in documenting the analysis performed, many months of elapsed time in discussions. This represents a significant drain on a company's resources at a time when no aircraft are being sold. With experience, however, this would be expected to reduce as the system is learnt.

CONDITION MONITORED MAINTENANCE (CAP 418)

Introduction

CAP 418 gives general information on the concepts and practices of aircraft maintenance control by the use of Condition Monitored Maintenance Programmes. The examples are complementary with BCAR Section A Chapter A6-4.

Airworthiness for these purposes is defined as 'the continuing capability of the aircraft to perform in a satisfactory manner the flight operations for which it was designed'. It is based on the expectation that flight operation will be performed with acceptable reliability in respect of flight crew work load, flight handling characteristics, flight performance, safety margins, welfare of occupants, punctuality, economics.

The document recognises the change in size, complexity and performance of aircraft, together with improved design techniques and a more knowledgeable approach to the control of maintenance. Traditional methods requiring fixed component lives and routine aircraft strip-down policies have given way to new techniques because they were no longer cost-effective, or were not appropriate to the design philosophy of modern aircraft.

Definition

Condition monitoring is defined as 'A primary maintenance process under which data on the whole population of specified items in service is analysed to indicate whether some allocation of technical resources is required. Not a preventive maintenance process, condition monitored maintenance allows failures to occur, and relies upon analysis of operating-experience information to indicate the need for appropriate action.' A further point to note is that failure modes of condition monitored items do not have a direct adverse effect on operating safety.

Condition monitoring is not a separate activity but a complete process which cannot be separated from the complete maintenance programme. It is not just an identification of a single maintenance action but is a basic maintenance philosophy. Maximum use can be made of the condition monitoring process which includes a statistical reliability element action when it is applied to aircraft meeting the following criteria:

Modern multi-engined, transport category aircraft which incorporate in their design safeguards against the complete loss of the function which a system is intended to perform. These safeguards are provided by either active redundancy or standby redundancy in the design of the aircraft or system. In an active redundancy philosophy all the redundant items are operating simultaneously and share the task; failure of a single item causes the task to be shared among the remaining items. In a standby redundancy philosophy only one redundant system is functioning at a time; if a failure occurs it is necessary to select a standby system.

Aircraft for which the initial scheduled maintenance programme has been specified by a maintenance review board and to which a maintenance steering group (MSG) logic analysis has been applied. Examples include the Boeing 747, Lockheed L1011, McDonnell Douglas DC-10.

For aircraft not covered by these criteria, the statistical reliability element of condition monitoring may be applied for the purpose of monitoring system or component performance, but may not be prescribed in the maintenance schedule as a primary maintenance process.

To use a statistical-reliability element of a programme effectively, CAP 418 specifies a fleet minimum of five aircraft to be normally necessary, depending on the aircraft type and utilisation. This means that some operators of the above wide-body aircraft would not be able to use such a programme, although other operators with larger fleets of identical types would be allowed to use a statistical reliability programme.

Primary maintenance

CAP 418 explains the three primary maintenance processes recognised by the UK CAA. They are hard time, on-condition, and condition monitoring. In general terms, the first two both involve actions directly concerned with preventing failure, whereas the last does not. The condition monitoring process is expected to lead to preventive actions if they are shown to be necessary.

Hard time

This is defined as a preventive process in which known deterioration of an item is limited to an acceptable level by the maintenance actions which are carried out at periods related to time in service. This time may be calendar time, number of cycles, or number of landings. The prescribed actions normally include servicing, full or partial overhaul, replacement according to instructions in the relevant documentation so that the item is restored to suitable condition for further use for a specified period.

On condition

This is also a preventive process, but one in which the item is inspected or tested at specified periods to an appropriate standard in order to determine whether it can continue in service. The inspection or test may reveal a need for servicing action. The fundamental purpose of on-condition is to remove an item before its failure in service. It is not a philosophy of 'use until failure'.

Condition monitoring

This is not a preventive process, having neither hard-time nor on-condition elements, but one in which information on items, gained from operational experience, is collected, analysed, and interpreted on a continuing basis as a means of implementing corrective procedures.

Where a MSG logic analysis has not been applied to a particular aircraft to establish and allocate the primary maintenance processes for each item, CAP 418 gives rules to be applied separately to all items to determine the acceptability of the primary maintenance processes. However, it is likely these days that most aircraft in use have been exposed to MSG logic from the design stage.

CAP 418 stresses the significance of the concept:

> Condition monitored maintenance, as a program, is the formalised application of the maintenance processes hard time, on-condition and condition monitoring to specific items as prescribed in the approved maintenance schedule. The controlling activity of condition monitored maintenance is condition monitoring irrespective of whether condition monitoring is prescribed as a primary maintenance process in the approved maintenance schedule or not. Condition monitoring is repetitive and continuous, the key factor in its use being the introduction of aircraft embodying failure tolerant designs, which allow for replacement of some traditional failure preventative maintenance techniques by non-preventive techniques. Condition monitoring is not a relaxation of maintenance standards or of airworthiness control; it is, in fact, more demanding of both management and engineering capabilities than the traditional preventive maintenance approaches. Each condition monitored maintenance program is required to be approved by the CAA.

A similar requirement applies to schemes approved by the US FAA.

This is quoted to show the lengthy explanation thought to be necessary by the CAA at the time of inception for such programmes. Traditional operation of hard time policies required adherence to fixed procedures by the maintenance organisation, with development being undertaken by engineering specialists to improve component lives. Condition monitoring requires more technical knowledge and understanding of the system behaviour from the maintenance staff themselves.

Maintenance activity

CAP 418 distinguishes three types of maintenance activity:

> Maintenance applied at specified periods of time regardless of condition at that time. The maintenance activity may be a periodic overhaul, change of parts, re-work, cleaning, calibration, lubrication, or some other recognised action. These result from hard-time requirements.

> Periodic examinations, mostly at specified periods of time, but sometimes on an opportunity basis, such as when an item is removed for access, to determine not only the extent of deterioration but also that the deterioration is within specified limits. These result from on-condition requirements.

> Actions in response to the analysis of condition clues by monitoring in-flight, hangar, workshop and other kinds of condition information sources. These result from condition monitoring requirements.

Condition monitoring uses data on failures as items of 'condition' information which are evaluated to establish a necessity for the production or variation of hard time and on-condition requirements, or for other corrective actions to be prescribed. Failure rates and effects are analysed to establish the need for corrective actions. Condition monitoring can be used in its own right to identify the effects of deterioration, in order that steps may be taken to maintain the level of reliability inherent in the design of the item. Although condition monitoring accepts that failures will occur, it is necessary to be selective in its application. The acceptance of failures may be governed by the relative unimportance of the function, or by the fact that the function is safeguarded by system redundancy.

Maintenance of a particular item could well be some combination of the above three primary maintenance activities. There is no hierarchy of these three; they are applied to the various items according to need and feasibility. Maintenance schedules which are based on the MSG principles will have hard time, on-condition, or condition monitoring specified as the primary maintenance process for specific systems and sub-systems as well as for individual maintenance significant items (MSIs). Condition monitoring can, therefore, be the primary maintenance process prescribed for an item, in which case it has also to be used for controlling the availability of those functions which are not directly controlled by a prescribed on-condition or hard time process; this control is provided by the statistical reliability element of condition monitored maintenance. Items for which hard time and on-condition are prescribed may, however, have the statistical reliability element of condition monitored maintenance applied, not as a primary maintenance process, but as a form of quality surveillance.

Statistical reliability element

The assessment of defect/removal/failure rate trend, of age bands at which items fail or the probability of survival to a given life are, in most cases, used to measure the effect or suitability of the primary maintenance processes applied to items. The assessment is made by examination of rates of occurrence of events such as in-flight defects, incidents, delays, use of redundancy capability, engine unscheduled shut-downs, air turnbacks, or other such measures, which are reported in accordance with the procedure associated with the reliability element of condition monitored maintenance.

A practical statistical reliability element does not need to be complicated or costly to establish or to operate. Some operators may be reluctant to adopt such a practice because they believe that computer systems are necessary. Computer-based recording and analysis may be an advantage, but it is not essential for these purposes.

Knowledge of probability is usually implied when discussing statistical techniques. Again, this is not essential here, where elementary data collection, summarising and display are needed. This is conveniently provided by modern computer software used for many business tasks. Comparison against established normal levels indicates the need for corrective action. This is not very different in principle from internal cost accounting and budgeting systems operated by other departments of an airline.

A condition monitored maintenance programme has two basic functions:

— To provide, by means of a statistical reliability element, a summary of aircraft fleet reliability reflecting the effectiveness of maintenance being done.
— To provide significant and timely technical information by which improvement may be achieved through changes to the programme or to the practices for implementing it.

A properly managed programme contributes not only to continuing airworthiness, but also to improvement of fleet reliability, to better long term planning, and to reduced overall costs.

Every programme is required to have a controlling body, which may be termed the reliability control committee, responsible for the implementation, decision making and daily running of the programme. It is essential that the committee should ensure that the programme establishes not only close co-operation between all relevant departments and personnel within the operators own organisation, but also liaison with other appropriate organisations. Lines of communication are to be defined and fully understood by all concerned. In practice this could be achieved by membership of the committee and by the circulations of its reports.

The reliability control committee is responsible for, and has the full authority to take, the necessary actions to implement the objectives and processes defined in the programme. It is normal for the quality manager or the engineering manager of the operator to head the committee and to be responsible to the CAA for the operation of the programme. The committee should meet frequently to review the programme and to discuss and resolve current problems. The committee should also ascertain that appropriate action is being taken in the normal progress of the programme and for corrective actions. Formal review meetings are held with the CAA at agreed intervals.

Data collection for the programme should depend on its needs. Suggested data for monitoring aircraft systems are pilot reports, engine unscheduled shutdowns, delays and cancellations attributed to mechanical failures. Data for component performance could be unscheduled removal rates, or workshop reports.

The objective of data collection is to identify quickly any adverse defect rate, trend, or apparent reduction in failure resistance and to direct the attention of specialists capable of remedying the fault.

Typical sources of data quoted are delay reports, in-flight defect reports, authorised operations with known defects, inoperative equipment levels compatible with the minimum equipment list (MEL), flight incidents, air turnbacks; line, hangar and workshop investigations. Other sources suggested are reports from on-condition tasks, airborne integrated data systems recordings, service bulletins, other operators' experience, and so on.

Statistical reliability measurement

Alert levels should be established for items controlled by the programme. Data such as pilot reports per 1,000 flying hours, unscheduled removal rates per 1,000 component hours, or whatever measure the committee finds suitable for this purpose, can be statistically analysed by the standard process quality-control methods. One example using an alert level of three standard deviations above the mean is shown in Table 3.1.

It is not essential to use this type of calculation; a simple factor above the mean may be adequate, such as defining alert level to be 1.3 times the mean level. In any case, with modern computers the labour of calculation and the graphical presentation is not a significant obstacle. It is more important that the method is understood and accepted by all involved in the programme than for theoretical methods to be used.

The alert level is intended to be an indicator, the exceedance of which is a deterioration of performance which must be investigated and acted upon. Alert levels for externally visible measures, such as delays and cancellations to scheduled services for engineering reasons, may be set by management decision in consultation with the marketing department.

Actuarial analysis

One further kind of statistical reliability analysis that is sometimes performed is the estimation of the age-related risk of failure, to determine whether or not a hard-time replacement policy is justifiable. The function being estimated has a variety of names

Table 3.1 Alert level example

Month	Events	3-months	Hours	3-mon. hrs	3-mon. rate
Nov	42		2400		
Dec	31		2320		
Jan	58	131	2350	7070	19
Feb	46	135	2300	6970	19
Mar	58	162	2560	7210	22
Apr	26	130	2600	7460	17
May	42	126	2750	7910	16
Jun	65	133	3100	8450	16
Jul	78	185	2880	8730	21
Aug	74	217	2700	8680	25
Sep	58	210	3000	8580	24
Oct	54	186	2650	8350	22
Nov	35	147	2610	8260	18
Dec	46	135	2330	7590	18
mean					19.8
standard deviation (s.d.)					3.2
3 × s.d. alert level					29

Fig. 3.2 Alert level plot

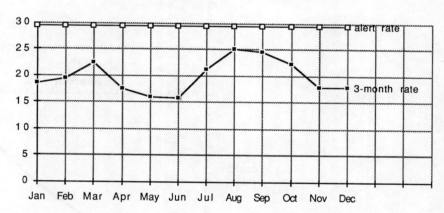

Pilot Reports per 1000 hours - System ATA 21

in reliability literature, these are 'age-specific failure rate', 'conditional failure rate', 'hazard rate', or 'hazard function'. It measures the failure rate of a component which has reached the age specified; in other words, the risk of instantaneous failure for a component that is no longer new.

Conventional statistical distribution functions described in most texts only show the age at failure for new (zero age) components. The maintenance engineer is more concerned with the trend in failure risk as the component ages. Thus, if wearout is suspected, the hazard function should show an increasing trend with ageing; only for this case will a hard-time policy of removing components at a predetermined age actually reduce the average failure rate for a population of these components. Other kinds of hazard function will either show no effect (constant hazard) or an actual increase in average failure rate (infant mortality).

The statistical analysis is performed by a technique similar to that used by insurance companies for estimating human life expectancy, hence the name actuarial analysis.

Fig. 3.3 Hazard function

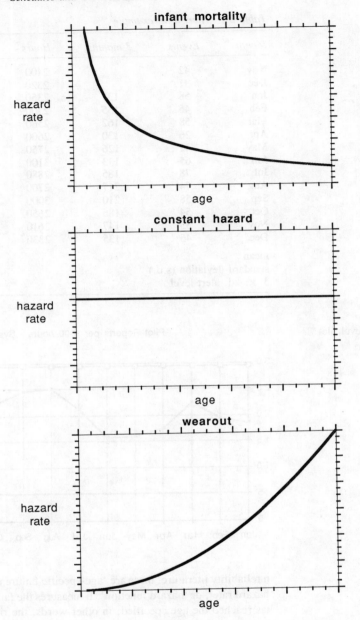

Because of this method, some engineers describe component behaviour by the 'bathtub curve', analogous to the human evidence of risk being least in middle life. However, it should be realised that the human model uses larger data samples than an aircraft engineer can obtain, and 'bathtub curves' in maintenance analysis are unlikely to be seen.

EXTENDED RANGE OPERATIONS (EROPS)

Extended range means operations beyond the original safety limit of flying time to the nearest airfield, with an engine failure. This is of particular significance with twin-engined aircraft, hence the title. The term extended range operations (EROPS) is also used; here they are considered to have the same meaning.

The UK version of these is described in CAP 513:

> The development of the modern turbofan engine has made it possible to extend the range of twin-engined aeroplanes to allow some of them to fly great distances.
>
> ... Whereas in the past it was necessary for regulatory bodies to consider only aircraft with three or more engines when recommending safe operating standards and practices for long-range flights, it has now become necessary to include twins in the reckoning.

Regulations

The original limit on the distance which a twin-engined aircraft might be from a suitable emergency airfield was set at 60 minutes flying time at normal single-engine cruise speed. Operations beyond this distance were described as 'extended range' and subject to special procedures, for which the maximum single-engine time was 120 minutes. An increase of 15 per cent on this figure, to a limit of 138 minutes, could be obtained after a qualifying period.

Experience with the 120 minute rule over several years has led to a further extension to a limit of 180 minutes flying time at single-engine speed. This is probably the maximum that will ever be allowed, since it enables flight over the remaining areas of the oceans not possible with the 120–138 minute rule.

Operators apply to the CAA for approval to operate at extended range. Aircraft manufacturers offer certain types as 'ER' versions, but they do not themselves obtain the operational approval. The design of these types must meet requirements specified for extended range operations before this approval is sought; the manufacturer is involved in the type approval process.

Maintenance impact

The implications for design and maintenance are stated in CAP 513:

1.6.1 A number of airframe and propulsion systems have an effect on the safety of extended range operations; therefore, the type design certification of the aeroplane will be reviewed, to ensure that the design of these systems is acceptable for the safe conduct of the intended operation.

...

1.6.3 Since the quality of maintenance programs can have an appreciable effect on the reliability of the propulsion systems and airframe systems required for extended range operation, an assessment will be made of the manufacturer's recommended and operator's proposed maintenance program's ability to maintain a satisfactory level of systems reliability for the particular airframe/ engine combination.

...

1.6.6 System redundancy levels appropriate to extended range operations will need to be reassessed and, where appropriate, reflected as revisions to minimum flight despatch configuration of the aeroplane.

The operator must demonstrate the ability to maintain the aeroplane to the required reliability.

The design of the aircraft must provide alternative power sources sufficient to permit continued safe flight in single-engine operation. Particular requirements are specified for electrical power, since automatic controls, instruments, navigation and communications depend on this. Possible supplies of emergency electrical power may be a flight-rated auxiliary power unit (APU), a hydraulic-powered generator, or a ram air turbine (RAT). The aircraft designer decides which of these are fitted. There are also special requirements for other systems that may need to provide longer protection, such as cargo hold fire suppression.

Another significant requirement for extended range aircraft is the in-service experience for acceptable propulsion systems. Only those that are considered to have reached maturity are considered; this is stated as 100,000 hours and 12 months experience for new engine types, less for derivatives. The primary measure of reliability is the inflight shutdown rate (IFSD); this should show a stable target value. The probability of dual engine failure for all independent causes in cruise must not exceed 0.3×10^{-8} per hour.

Airline engineering and maintenance requirements

These are described under several headings:

1. *Engineering modifications*
   Modifications particular to EROPS must be identified to the Authority. Assessment should consider their impact on these operations.
2. *Maintenance and training*
   Procedures, practices and limitations established for EROPS should be approved.
3. *Reliability reporting*
   A programme should be developed before approval and continued afterwards. Regular reports must be sent to the Authority and manufacturer.
4. *Modifications and inspections*
   Procedures for prompt implementation of modifications and inspections affecting propulsion system reliability must exist.
5. *Aircraft despatch*
   An aircraft should not fly an extended range operation after a power unit shutdown or primary system failure has occurred on a previous flight, or after significant adverse trends in system performance, unless appropriate corrective action has been taken. A successful flight subsequent to the corrective action may be needed to confirm this.
6. *Maintenance programme*
   The operator must ensure that aircraft, engine and equipment reliability are maintained at the level required for EROPS.
7. *Engine condition monitoring*
   This must be developed, and may include hard-time inspection intervals for component condition not observable and which may affect failure rates.
8. *Oil consumption*
   This must be monitored for engines, and for the APU as that is part of the emergency power system.

Flight despatch

Although an operations department function, this also has engineering implications for EROPS.

Minimum equipment list (MEL)

For EROPS, the aircraft minimum equipment list must reflect the required reliability, and will almost certainly be different from that for other operations with the same aircraft type. Primary system redundancy levels must be adequate; primary systems are defined as those which have a fundamental influence on flight safety and could be adversely affected by the shutdown of a power unit.

Maintenance requirements

CAP 513 states:

Plate 7 Servicing a turbofan engine

The maintenance program should contain the standards, guidance, and direction necessary to support the intended operations. Maintenance personnel involved should be made aware of the special nature of EROPS and have the knowledge, skills and ability to accomplish the requirements of the program.

The maintenance programme for EROPS should be based on the same maintenance schedule as approved for other operations. The schedule should be reviewed to ensure provision for EROPS requirements. Procedures should preclude identical action being applied to multiple similar elements critical to EROPS, for example, a fuel control change on both engines.

EROPS related tasks should be identified as such in the operator's routine work forms. A special service check should be developed for critical items; this should be signed by an EROPS qualified person immediately prior to an EROPS flight. The technical log should ensure adherence to proper minimum equipment list procedures, deferred items and maintenance checks.

Plate 8 Powerplant
preparation bay

The operator should develop a manual for use by EROPS personnel. This should indicate where the necessary requirements are found in the operator's other documents. All EROPS requirements, procedures, duties and responsibilities should be identified and subject to revision control. Alternatively the operator may include this information in existing manuals used by personnel involved in EROPS.

The operator should have an oil consumption programme in accordance with manufacturer's recommendations, and capable of reacting to trends. It should be a continuous programme; if oil analysis is relevant to the engine type, it should be part of it. If the APU is required for EROPS, its oil consumption should be monitored by the programme.

Engine condition monitoring (ECM) should be a program reflecting manufacturer's instructions and industry practice, specifying the method of data collection and corrective action process. This monitoring is intended to detect deterioration at an early stage to allow for corrective action before safe operation is affected. The programme should ensure that engine limit margins are maintained so that a prolonged single-engine diversion may be conducted without exceeding approved engine limits, such as rotor speed or gas temperature, at all approved power levels and expected environmental conditions. Engine margins preserved through this program should account for the effects of additional engine-loading demands such as anti-icing, or electrical, which may be required during the single-engine flight phase associated with the diversion.

The operator should develop a programme or procedures to ensure corrective action following an engine shutdown, primary system failure, adverse trends, or any prescribed events which require verification flight or other action, and establish means to assure their accomplishment. A clear description of who must initiate verification actions, and of the section or group responsible for the determination of what action is necessary, should be identified in the programme. Primary systems or conditions requiring verification actions should be described in the operator's EROPS manual.

An EROPS reliability programme should be developed, or the existing reliability programme supplemented. This programme should be designed with early identification and prevention of EROPS-related problems as the primary goal. The programme should be event-oriented and incorporate reporting procedures for significant events detrimental to EROPS flights. This information should be readily available for use by the operator and the Authority to help establish that the reliability level is adequate, and to assess the operator's competence and capability to continue ETOPS safely. The Authority should be notified within 96 hours of events reportable through this programme.

AGEING AIRCRAFT

Introduction

The 'old age' problem for civil jet transports has now been under active discussion for many years; an example is Ramsden (1981), when 15 years of age and 50,000 flying hours were thought to be high-time figures for an aircraft. The Lusaka accident in 1977 emphasised some of the factors involved, namely fail-safe design, fatigue testing, corrosion prevention, inspection methods, and maintenance action.

Ten years later we are still talking about the 'ageing aircraft' issue, except that the qualification period is now 20 years since manufacture and 60,000 flying hours use, and the event regarded as having the most significant influence is the Aloha Airlines accident in 1988. This again brought into question established thinking about design, certification, corrosion, fatigue, inspection and maintenance. (Details of both accidents will be found in Chapter 7.)

Statistics

Some statistics about aircraft ages are shown in the tables. These show numbers of aircraft for various manufacturers relative to the 'economic design life', which is a target value used by the designers in setting a balance between first costs, payload capacity, and maintenance costs. There is no absolute predetermined maximum age for a modern airliner; as age and fatigue increase, possibly with additional corrosion effects, inspection reveals more flaws that need repair and thus the maintenance cost rises until (in theory) it should be cheaper to buy a new aircraft than to retain the old one.

Early jet transports exhibited a variety of design philosophies; some favoured high payload at the expense of structural life, some favoured structural durability at the expense of payload, some established higher first cost to the benefit of maintenance costs. Many of these early types of the 1960s were pure jet-engined with high fuel consumption. This did not matter in the era of low fuel costs and high fares, but the oil price rises of the 1970s altered this. The airlines' first response to the dual problem of rising costs and shrinking markets, caused by the sharp energy price increases and economic recession, was to retire these thirsty aircraft, or to modify them with newer turbofan engines if the structure was sound enough to justify the investment. Thus, to some extent, the problem of high-age aircraft was deferred until the late 1970s.

Table 3.2 Boeing commercial jet aircraft fleet status, late 1989

Model	Active fleet	Design life (economic)	Numbers over % of design life	
			75%	100%
707	342	20,000 cycles	266	109
		60,000 hours	236	68
		20 years	201	165
727	1,766	60,000 cycles	262	13
		50,000 hours	334	446
		20 years	841	721
737	1,547	75,000 cycles	99	1
		51,000 hours	257	85
		20 years	297	209
747	595	20,000 cycles	112	11
		60,000 hours	205	105
(excl. -SP, -SR)		20 years	202	4

Table 3.3 McDonnell Douglas commercial jet fleet status in 1988

Model	Active fleet	Design life (economic)	Numbers over this design life
DC8	350	25,000 cycles	49
		50,000 hours	203
		20 years	350
DC9	924	40,000 cycles	504
		30,000 hours	636
		20 years	184
MD80	496	50,000 cycles	0
		50,000 hours	0
		20 years	0
DC10	425	42,000 cycles	0
		60,000 hours	0
		20 years	0

Table 3.4 Jet transport aircraft 20 years old or more

Make	Model	1989	1995	2000
Airbus	A300	0	20	125
Boeing	707/720	337	397	435
	727	737	1,123	1,647
	737	221	419	699
	747	31	265	487
British Aerospace	BAC111	159	196	211
Fokker	F28	10	84	144
Lockheed	L1011	0	123	193
McDonnell Douglas	DC8	299	342	342
	DC9	511	745	894
	DC10	0	202	328
	MD80	0	0	7
All others	—	135	186	219
Total	—	2,440	4,102	5,731

(*Aviation Week*, 24 July 1989; assumes no further losses or retirement)

Table 3.5 Airbus design objectives and service history

Model	Fleet	Design life (economic)	Numbers over	
			25%	*50%*
A300B4	237	36,000 cycles (60,000 hours)	178	34
A300-600	58	30,000 cycles (67,500 hours)	10	0
A310	149	35,000 cycles (60,000 hours)	14	0
A320	23	48,000 cycles (60,000 hours)	0	0
A330	—	40,000 cycles (60,000 hours)	—	—
A340	—	20,000 cycles (30,000 hours)	—	—

(*Source*: *Flight International*)

Increase in older aircraft numbers

As implied, the 'economic life' concept should have taken care of ageing aircraft by removing them from service. In fact this has not happened to the extent expected by aircraft manufacturers. One Boeing statement quoted an estimated 250 to 300 ageing transports to be retired in 1988, but only 60 were disposed of. Among the reasons for this postponement are:

— The higher costs of new aircraft, certificated to stricter standards such as ICAO Annex 16 Chapter 3 noise levels, and tougher structural regulations.
— Price inflation which makes new aircraft appear much more expensive than the existing ones, written down at historical costs only.
— Increasing travel demands, which have made it necessary for replacements to be larger or more numerous.
— Price competition and market share battles, which have lowered fares and reduced profitability.
— Shortage of aircraft available from manufacturers, which has extended delivery times years into the future.

Ageing aircraft programme

Although the Aloha accident in 1988 dramatised the possible consequences of high-age aircraft, the subject was under active study by the industry before this event. The FAA-sponsored Ageing Aircraft Conference took place in June 1988 at Washington, DC. This established the working groups with the responsibility of examining each manufacturer's products, to prepare inspections and modifications to restore structural safety of the airframes. The working groups reviewed all service bulletins issued for age-related work and selected those considered to be essential; these became mandatory modifications. Factors considered in this selection were safety effects, failure risk, and inspection difficulty. Implementation targets were set at flight cycles, aircraft hours, or calendar time, depending on whether the damage was related to fatigue or corrosion. Most of these limits were the same as the original economic design lives, a few were lower. Thus, to exceed the economic life of an aircraft type, an operator would first have to perform extra work to that specified in the approved maintenance schedule.

Many of the surveys were only completed in late 1989, and have effective dates

Plate 9 Boeing 747 major
structural overhaul

up to four years beyond the issue date of the directive. Work on the older aircraft
will therefore occupy operators for much of the 1990s, should they decide to keep
the aircraft. This means that by the mid-1990s, for instance, there could be over 200
Boeing 747 aircraft exceeding the original economic design life. Since a new 747
is very expensive, and Boeing only offer the larger 400-series aircraft from 1990
onwards, operators wanting less costly or smaller-capacity versions are likely to choose
a refurbished aircraft. Provision of spare parts needed in the high-age modifications
is handled by the manufacturers for key parts requiring special machining or by
approved maintenance organisations for some less critical parts. Supply difficulties
may develop as operators place orders after preliminary inspection. Corrosion repairs
have been cited as a particular source of forecasting errors, because objective standards

for corrosion control have not been set. Some operators believe that prevention is better than cure, others prefer to wait for evidence before acting. To deal with this, a separate corrosion control programme has been developed.

Corrosion control programme

The FAA-proposed corrosion control programme for ageing Boeing aircraft, and the adopted final recommendations on limiting structural fatigue, announced in April 1990, are both outcomes of the Ageing Aircraft Task Force, a US government/industry safety coalition formed after the failure of the Aloha airlines Boeing 737 fuselage in April 1988.

The fatigue-related directives essentially followed recommendations issued by the task force in 1989 covering McDonnell Douglas and Boeing aircraft. Recommendations on Lockheed L1011 aircraft and on other manufacturers' aircraft followed. As with the fatigue directives, the corrosion programme was developed with the close co-operation of Boeing and various airlines, and is therefore likely to be implemented without substantial changes.

The new programme establishes three levels of corrosion. Level 1 is the type of corrosion that 'occurs in a good program', according to the FAA deputy director of aircraft certification service. Level 1 corrosion was described as 'a fact of life' by the associate administrator for regulation and certification, being inevitable from the moment the aircraft is built. Airlines with aircraft having Level 1 corrosion will have no special reporting or repair requirements imposed on them.

Level 2 corrosion is considered a warning sign. This would be excessive corrosion that exceeds allowable limits, taking place between regular inspection intervals. It requires repairs or replacement of parts, and may also approach allowable rework limits.

The main purpose in establishing Level 2 corrosion is to warn operators that an aircraft is approaching Level 3. That is defined as corrosion found to be 'a potential airworthiness concern', requiring prompt corrective action. Level 3 corrosion 'generally is a sign that the corrosion control program is not doing its job', the deputy director said. One example would be the widespread corrosion in a fuselage that could exceed its structural limits.

Under the proposed directive, the FAA establishes that an effective maintenance programme is one that limits corrosion of all primary aircraft structure to Level 1. To assist the FAA in monitoring compliance with this, all airlines with corrosion in their fleet at Levels 2 and 3 must report to Boeing, where the data will be compiled for use by the FAA.

The FAA estimated the costs of the Boeing programme, but emphasised that these represented the lowest possible figures, the actual expense will probably be higher — for example:

— Boeing 707: $81,000 per aircraft, amounting to about $32M world-wide if all other authorities follow FAA recommendations;
— Boeing 727: $80,000 per aircraft, $137M world-wide;
— Boeing 737: $39,000 per aircraft, $23M world-wide;
— Boeing 747: $190,000 per aircraft, $54M world-wide.

Early estimates from actual experience quote increases of up to 100 per cent initially, and then up to 50 per cent recurring for the heavy maintenance checks on some older aircraft. Other sources claim increases of around $5M to $10M on the maintenance cost for ageing-aircraft modifications. Companies with design authority may have an advantage, and third-party maintenance organisations are looking at the market for contract work.

The corrosion control programme establishes many inspection areas for each aircraft. Each area comprises numerous zones; repairs and inspections are made at zone level. A typical corrosion repair would require removing the damaged surface down to the undamaged metal and then fitting a patch or protective coating.

Special corrosion inspections are required for aircraft after their 15th year of service. Every airline has to inspect the equivalent of one aircraft for each area. The sampling programme guarantees that every area receives inspection once yearly on a B737; for instance, whether or not maintenance is planned in that area at less frequent intervals.

Cost comparisons

As examples of the attraction of older aircraft, Table 3.6 and Fig. 3.4 give some extracts from reported industry data collected by Avmark, Inc.

Table 3.6   25-year-old DC8-71 vs 6-year-old B767-300 costs

Aircraft operating data, year ending 30 June 1989 (industry average)		
Aircraft	*DC8-71*	*B767-300*
Average fleet size	29.0	28.8
Flight distance, km	2,039	2,165
Flight block time, hr	3.09	3.25
Utilisation, block hr/day	9.4	12.3
Average seats	199	232
Costs (US $ per block hr)		
Crew, salaries, etc.	582	571
Fuel, oil & taxes	883	823
Maintenance:		
Airframe	252	110
Engine	117	82
Total direct maintenance	369	192
Maintenance burden	271	71
Total maintenance cost	639	263
Cash operating expenses	2,112	1,680
Depreciation and rentals	402	1,268
Total A'C operating expense	$2,514	$2,948
Cost/revenue-mile, US $	6.1	7.1
Cost/seat-km, US ¢	1.91	1.90

Fig. 3.4 Cost comparison, DC8 vs B767

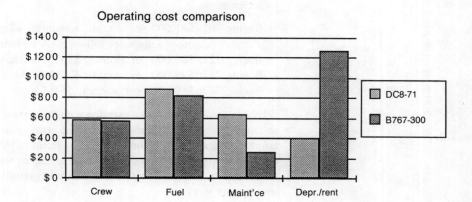

70

Table 3.7 Old DC9 vs new MD-80 aircraft cost estimates

Operating costs	Old DC9-30	New MD-82
Average flight, n.m.	500	500
Flights per year	2,110	2,110
Capital cost, $M	6.5	25
Interest rate, p.a.	10%	10%
Costs (US $/block hr)		
Flight crew	590	614
Cabin crew	285	419
Maintenance	514	545
Fuel	613	701
Landing fees	162	224
Capital cost	300	1,200
Total	$2,464	$3,703
Seats	97	143
Cost/available seat-mile	¢5.1	¢5.2

Fig. 3.5 Cost comparison, DC9 vs MD-80

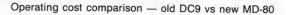

Operating cost comparison — old DC9 vs new MD-80

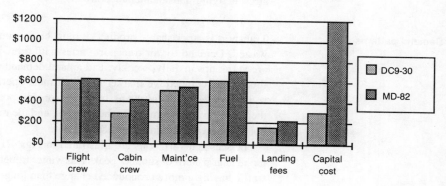

These are not entirely typical; the DC8-71 was re-engined with quieter, lower fuel consumption engines some years ago, but this was only considered worthwhile because the good condition of the airframe gave a return on the investment. No more airframes are available, so an operator using them will not sell.

Another example, estimated (Table 3.7), shows the difficulty that aircraft designers now face in producing real improvements for some types. Without the great expansion in traffic and the technical incentives of noise regulations, it would be hard to sell new aircraft.

Evidence of this difficulty was the suspension of the Boeing and McDonnell Douglas aircraft projects using propfans or 'unducted fans'. The lower fuel consumption did not attract airline orders.

CHAPTER 4 MAINTENANCE PRODUCTION

AIRLINE SCHEDULING — WITH REFERENCE TO ENGINEERING

Commercial requirements of aircraft availability

The main task of the airline engineer is to produce serviceable aircraft to support the flying programme of the airline, or tour company. This schedule is determined largely by commercial requirements, with allowance made for factors such as aircrew duty legislation, airport capacity, competition from other operators and other modes of transport. Some of the factors which have to be taken into account in scheduling aircraft flying and maintenance are:

Demand patterns

Transport is a perishable product, it must be consumed at the time of production or wasted. Demand for air transport varies with time, as for many other goods. There are variations in daily, weekly, and annual demand which result in peaks at popular times. The competitive market in which most operators now work results in them trying to meet these peaks as far as reasonably possible. Aircraft availability has, therefore, to be maximised at these peaks, and the maintenance fitted into spare time not required for commercial activities.

The seasonal variations are illustrated in Figs 4.1 to 4.3. Passenger traffic shows the regular pattern of summer peaks and winter troughs, with short-haul (UK—Europe) traffic having a more pronounced change than long-haul. Note that these figures are for scheduled flights only, and that charter traffic has even greater seasonal variation. In the UK, charter operations are about 30 per cent of the total industry output in tonne-km. Cargo traffic exhibits a different pattern, responding to business cycles instead of holidays.

Seasonal effects

Air transport being mostly a leisure-oriented industry today, travel demand follows seasonal variations. In the Northern hemisphere this means that the summer months are busier than the winter for most operators. On some routes, such as to and from holiday resorts, the ratio of peak-month to low-month travel is large. Operators will want to arrange heavy maintenance, which takes an aircraft out of service for weeks, outside the summer peaks. There are also shorter peaks, such as annual national holidays, which greatly increase the demand for aircraft. On a shorter timescale, there are daily and weekly fluctuations of demand, such as the morning/afternoon peaks favoured by businessmen, and the weekend preference of leisure travellers. These short-term cycles have a strong effect on short-haul routes, and make it difficult for operators to achieve a high aircraft utilisation.

Summer

Summer for most airlines is the busiest period of the year, but its length may vary round the world. Most operators try to minimise routine maintenance in the summer,

Passenger million ton–kilometres
UK airlines scheduled traffic
6.7% p.a. growth rate
700
600
500
400
300
200
100
0
million tonne-km
1972 1974 1976 1978 1980 1982 1984 1986 1988 1990
Year

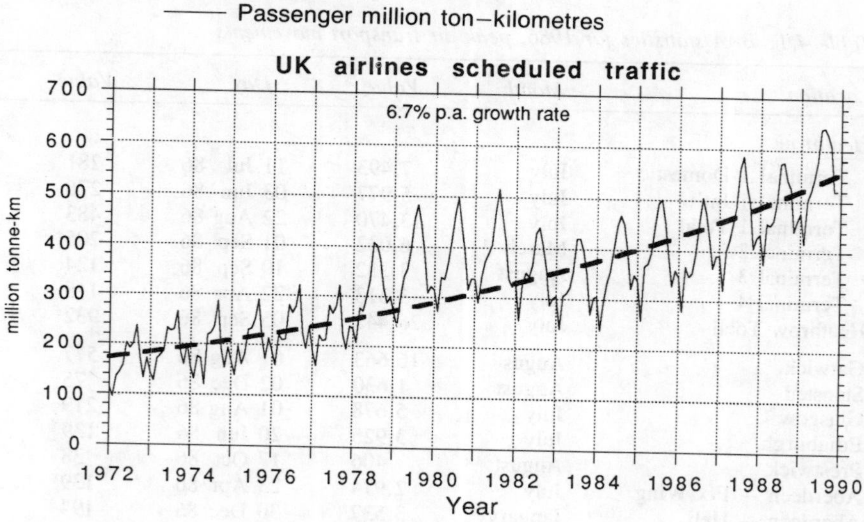

Fig. 4.1 Monthly UK passenger traffic, years 1972–89

Cargo million ton–kilometres
UK airlines scheduled traffic
7.4% p.a. growth rate
250
200
150
100
50
0
million tonne-km
1972 1974 1976 1978 1980 1982 1984 1986 1988 1990
Year

Fig. 4.2 Monthly UK cargo traffic, years 1972–89

Air to Europe
Air to rest of world
UK passenger movements quarterly
18
16
14
12
10
8
6
4
2
millions
1986 1987 1988 1989 1990
year

Fig. 4.3 Quarterly UK passenger movements, years 1986–9

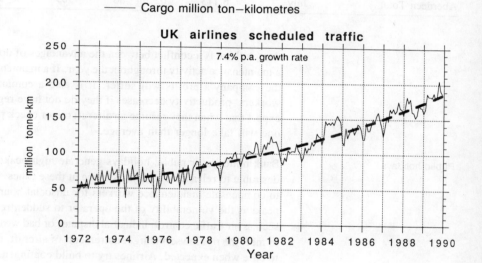

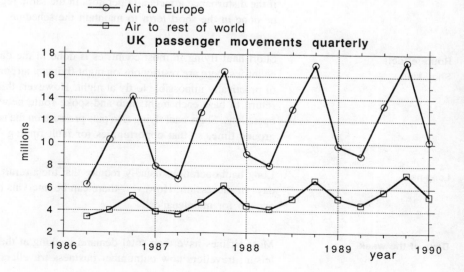

Table 4.1 *BAA statistics for 1986, peak air transport movements*

Location	Month	Value	Day	Value	Annual	Peak/Average	
						Month	Day
Heathrow							
Terminal 1 Domestic	July	7,493	11 Jul 86	281			
Terminal 1 Int'l	July	5,977	03 Jun 86	276			
Terminal 1 Total	July	13,470	22 Aug 86	483			
Terminal 2	March	6,032	01 Sep 86	205			
Terminal 3	August	3,332	10 Sep 86	124			
Terminal 4	July	3,313	22 Apr 86	118			
Heathrow Total	July	26,443	05 Sep 86	932	289,300	1.10	1.18
Gatwick	August	16,663	01 Aug 86	577	154,700	1.29	1.36
Stansted	August	1,630	02 Dec 86	75	16,000	1.22	1.71
Glasgow	July	5,678	01 Aug 86	219	56,500	1.21	1.41
Edinburgh	July	3,925	20 Jun 86	139	36,600	1.29	1.39
Prestwick	August	406	17 Oct 86	38	2,800	1.74	4.95
Aberdeen — Fix Wing	July	2,974	23 Apr 86	139	32,100	1.11	1.58
Aberdeen — Heli.	January	3,537	30 Dec 86	194	36,100	1.18	1.96
Aberdeen Total	July	6,113	02 Jul 86	303	78,200	0.94	1.41

though there is a conflict between the advantages of doing this and those of running a maintenance activity throughout the year. If a maintenance base is not fully utilised, the company's profits will suffer. It is also a common industrial experience that workers' productivity decreases if they do not have regular activity. Most operators expect that when they resume an aircraft major check pattern, after a break, the first one will take longer than average.

Public holidays

Bank holidays or public holidays generate high peaks lasting for a few days. It is desirable to release aircraft for service at these times. This may also avoid the need to compensate maintenance workers for unsocial hours. A further problem of such peaks is the vulnerability of the operator to sudden restrictions outside his control, such as air traffic control, industrial disputes or bad weather. This can make it difficult to meet the routine servicing requirements of aircraft, especially if they do not return to base when expected. Airlines try to build contingency factors into their plans, but if the disturbance affects all operators in the same region there is not much that can be done in the short term to maintain the schedule.

Route effects
Short-haul

Short-haul flying in most countries is done in the daytime; in many industrialised countries there are restrictions on night flying at airports which make it economically or practically impossible to fly at night. However, this also means that most aircraft return to base each night; hub-and-spoke route networks are typical of short-haul operations. Short-haul flying also puts pressure on the need to reduce scheduled aircraft ground time, so that opportunities for fault-finding during the day are limited.

Long-haul

Long-haul operations usually require that the aircraft is away from base for several days in succession. However, there can be intervals between flights which are long enough for maintenance.

Days of the week

Most airlines have their total demand peaking at the opening of a weekend, since leisure travellers now outnumber business travellers, as a whole.

Within the weekly cycle, there will be less busy days into which some maintenance work may be fitted.

British airlines have lowest demand in the midweek period, particularly on Tuesdays. This is frequent enough to be part of a regular plan.

Timing

Commercial timing is often regarded as important for marketing reasons. Study of timetables or airport movements indicates that airlines try to manoeuvre their schedules to take advantage of this.

Business travel has a morning peak coinciding with the normal working day, and for the same reason there is a desire to return at the end of the day.

Some services have built up a following over a long period, such that operators feel reluctant to change the advertised times.

For promotional purposes, it is thought easier to have departures which are hourly events, or at other easily-remembered intervals.

Flights are often scheduled to fit in with others, for example transatlantic arrivals in Europe connect with a following shorter flight. Long-haul flights must link up to give the passenger his total journey in a reasonable time, otherwise the advantage of air travel will be lost.

Turnrounds

Aircraft only earn money when they are flying. The reduction of unnecessary dead time on the ground is now the objective of most schedulers. This may lead to an aircraft operating different routes during a day.

Configurations

Airlines vary their seating and loading plans according to the market. For inclusive-tour charters and other low-fare promotions, high-density seating is required. For business-class travel and high-revenue routes, low-density seating is necessary. There are also different passenger—cargo mixes possible on some aircraft, such as the 'combi' with passengers and freight on the same deck.

Configuration changes

Interior configuration changes require removal of seats and possibly other alterations to furnishing, galleys, and inflight entertainment. The schedule should be constructed to minimise the frequency of this work where possible.

Maintenance opportunities

Maintenance opportunities will vary with the nature of the operations and the market. The scheduler has to make the best use of these.

Preferred maintenance times

If commercial reasons are considered, the best occasions for maintenance are:

Short-haul operations

Overnight maintenance of short-haul aircraft enables most short-term routine scheduled work and unscheduled work to be performed satisfactorily.

Many short-haul routes are used for business or commuter travel. There is less demand for the aircraft at weekends, so routine work which takes longer than an overnight visit can be done then.

The quieter midweek period can be used for maintenance inputs of about one or two days duration.

Larger short-haul aircraft

Larger aircraft are usually flown on the busy inclusive-tour charters which peak in the summer. There is therefore time in the winter for major checks and other long tasks to be done on these aircraft.

Economic short-haul aircraft

Aircraft that yield the highest profits should be used most frequently. This means, therefore, that they are fully committed to flying during the summer peaks. Winter maintenance is best for these aircraft. These aircraft are usually the newer purchases, since the higher depreciation charges make it necessary to fly them intensively.

Long-haul operations

The long-haul summer peak can last many months; it is desirable that heavy maintenance activity is scheduled outside this period.

Weekend availability for long-haul aircraft must be highest. Maintenance should therefore avoid the Friday to Sunday period if possible. This provides a longer maintenance period than the short-haul midweek.

There may be sufficiently long intervals during daytime long-haul aircraft turnrounds to perform maintenance. This is not always at the home base.

Long-haul aircraft

Again, the larger aircraft are in greater demand during the summer, so winter maintenance is preferable for these types.

Aircraft with unusual routes or performance, such as supersonic or ultra-long range types, may not have the same peak patterns as others. Luxury markets tend to have weak demand in the high summer, so maintenance can be done then.

Maintenance — ideal production requirements

A different set of objectives from that of the commercial requirements emerges if aircraft maintenance is examined from the production engineer's standpoint. Reconciling these conflicts in the best way is the art of good scheduling.

Scheduled work

Scheduled work is predictable and regular; it obeys the same laws as found in the rest of the production industry. This means minimising learning-curve losses, reducing inventory levels and balancing the workload between different tasks.

The ideal situation is to imitate in the airline the production-line system used in manufacture. In maintenance, the aircraft stays in the same location rather than moving

Plate 10 Undercarriage work during major check

down a line, but otherwise the same rules apply. Work is planned in advance, often years ahead.

If there are always aircraft under maintenance, then workers can be almost continuously engaged. Shift patterns can be set up for a long period and the necessary industrial agreements need not be revised too often.

Painting a modern aircraft to the standard required by most operators requires specialised equipment and processes which are not easy to use on a normal maintenance dock. Most large airlines therefore favour a separate paint bay in its own hangar. This represents a considerable investment which must be fully utilised.

Shift work has disadvantages for operators in most industrialised countries. It requires extra payments and additional negotiations with staff. Minimising dependence on shift work, except in emergencies, is sought by most operators.

Just as the hangar maintenance supports the flying programme, so the workshop maintenance supports the hangar programme for many aircraft parts. The same considerations, therefore, apply to workshop flow as to aircraft sequencing. Sudden peak demands for major rework should be avoided.

It is desirable for large airframe parts such as flaps, control surfaces, doors and similar units, which may generate problems in interchangeability with other aircraft, to be returned to the aircraft from which they came. This requires agreement with the workshop or outside contractor on the schedule for receiving and returning the components. Otherwise spare parts will have to be obtained to cover the aircraft maintenance programme.

If demand is known well in advance, then parts needed in routine replacements can be ordered in good time and delivered to the workplace. Otherwise more inventory is needed to protect against uncertain demand.

Unscheduled work

Unscheduled work arises in the operation of aircraft, which are complicated machines with many possibilities for behaviour outside the specification, which by their nature are difficult to forecast. The solution is to make some provision for them, based on experience, and to manipulate them when they occur. (This policy is considered in more detail elsewhere.) There are various methods available to operators for dealing with unscheduled maintenance work.

Allowable deficiency use

Modern aircraft have considerable redundancy built into them, in the form of standby components; systems that are duplicated, triplicated, or even more; units that are not needed for every flight; units used below their maximum rating; and other features in excess of the minimum requirement. By agreement with airworthiness authorities, operators have the ability to class some minor defects as 'allowable deficiencies', which can be rectified at more convenient opportunities instead of requiring immediate attention.

An aircraft has a set of minimal requirements which must be satisfied before every flight is despatched. This is laid down as part of the operating rules in the Minimum Equipment List (MEL). Maintenance activity should obviously concentrate on meeting these needs as priority.

Unscheduled work which may be deferred is done at convenient times. These follow much the same descriptions as for scheduled work, with the provision that a maximum time limit may apply to some deferred defects before they are corrected.

Most airlines are round-the-clock operations. The staff supporting unscheduled maintenance work are therefore rostered on a shift pattern according to the expected demand. Contingency plans to handle unscheduled work should therefore recognise these opportunities and their capacity.

Since unscheduled maintenance arises as part of the flying programme, when the aircraft are expected to be out of base, it is likely that hangar capacity will be available for unscheduled work. Conditions in a hangar are more conducive to efficient work than out on a ramp or apron.

The logistics mission

The task of the airline scheduler may be formally stated as a logistics mission: 'to ensure that at all times the airline operating plan is optimally structured and resourced to achieve the maximum profitability whilst delivering standards of excellence in customer service' (R. Bolt).

Support of the optimal airline operating plan

A Logistics Branch in the airline would report to the Operations Director and consist of sections having the responsibilities:

— user requirements;
— operations and maintenance planning;
— flight crew planning;
— cabin crew planning;
— fleet planning and evaluation;
— scheduling.

In this way, the functions of different departments in the airline are brought together to focus on the problems of constructing and operating the schedule. The reason for doing this is to avoid the inter-departmental disputes which often arise in operators whose organisations are vertically divided, up to general manager level, into the more traditional functions of engineering, operations and commercial activities.

The airline product

Nowadays, it is usual for airline executives to speak of the 'airline product', a term which embraces the complete task, from conception and presentation to the customer, through to the actual implementation and follow-up. People used to talk of 'tourist class', 'business class', and other divisions as if only the seating accommodation and service were important. In practice, market segmentation is achieved by altering the conditions of sale for tickets and the standard of service, to attract various types of customer. Bookings for these different markets are monitored by computer reservation systems to ensure control over the allocation in accordance with policy.

Customer expectation

Services offered range from those with high standards of cabin service, for VIP customers, through those with medium cabin-service standards with emphasis on frequency and reliability of departure, for business travellers, to simpler service classes with emphasis on lower fares and advance booking, to suit leisure travellers. More than one class of service will be available on the same aircraft, making it necessary to have divided cabins and different galleys.

Charter

Charter flights are made either by specialist operators or by charter divisions of an airline. Thus the charter aircraft is bought and equipped for this purpose and fully committed to such operations. It is therefore difficult to switch aircraft between charters and scheduled services, even on a long-term basis. Scheduled operators may, however, charter or lease aircraft to fill in shortfalls in their own fleet. Similarly, operators with great variations in seasonal traffic may find other uses for their aircraft in the low season, in other parts of the world.

Internal and external factors

In scheduling, the airline faces many factors, some of internal origin and others from external sources. Internal factors are the organisation, equipment and staff of the company. External factors are the airport and air traffic control, airworthiness regulation systems, the state of the economy, other airlines and modes of transport in competition, and even other forms of communication for business or of recreation for leisure. Internal factors are, in theory, known to the airline and under its control. External factors may be discovered by market research, routine consultation with representatives of the organisations providing the service and by regular notices from such bodies.

Large airlines may attempt to influence external factors by using full-time staff to lobby governments, trade associations and other suppliers.

Some of the internal factors have been mentioned before, they include:

Marketing

The operator has agreed to carry passengers or freight, either directly by contract with a tour operator or forwarder, or implicitly by advertising its services to the public.

Operations control

The operator has a main base of operations, with secondary bases for aircraft servicing and overhaul. Suppliers of serviceable aircraft and parts may be located at the home base, or at other bases further away.

Engineering

The number and variety of aircraft types used by the operator will dictate the plans made for support of the flying programme. Operators may rely largely on their own staff and equipment for servicing, or they may use contractors.

Air crew

Flight-crew duty times are controlled by legislation, but companies may also have industrial relations agreements which affect the use of crew.

Cabin-crew numbers are fixed by regulations related to aircraft size. Again, there may be company agreements on the duty and remuneration of staff which have to be monitored.

Ground operations

Ground operations at most airports are managed by the operator, subject to the limitations of airport managements. Some airports provide services to operators, others leave operators to make their own arrangements.

Marketing requirements

The essential requirement of the marketing department may be stated by the common phrase 'The right aircraft in the right place at the right time at the right price'. If disturbances to the schedule occur after the plan, it is necessary to meet this requirement in the best way, by revising the plan or by leasing aircraft.

Aircraft types available

Most operators have different types of aircraft, to suit the different kinds of service they provide, or because old and new aircraft are used. Examples of these in commercial aircraft are:

Wide-body

This includes the Boeing 747, McDonnell Douglas DC10 and its successor the MD-11, Lockheed TriStar (L1011), Boeing 767, larger Airbus (A300). Wide-body usually means twin-aisle seating layouts in the passenger cabin, 7-abreast and upwards. Wide-body aircraft form a distinct group in the airline for crewing and maintenance purposes, owing to the geographical separation from base.

Some aircraft are large because of the volume of traffic on a route. Smaller DC10s, TriStars, Airbus and Boeing 767s are examples.

Aircraft used on the world's main routes, such as transatlantic or transpacific operations, include the Boeing 747s, larger DC10s, newer long-range Boeing 767s and Airbus. A few specialist versions of the Boeing 747 (SP) and TriStar (-500) are in service for very long ranges; the Boeing 747-400, McDonnell Douglas MD-11 and Airbus 340 will become the main equipment of airlines interested in longer routes.

Short-range

Short-range aircraft in the jet-powered class extend down to 100-seaters. They may be used by large airlines for high-frequency business class travel, and leisure travel to resorts with small airports, or by small 'niche' carriers. Aircraft below 100 seats passenger capacity are predominantly turboprops and are usually operated by specialist commuter carriers, often in association with a neighbouring larger carrier. All short-range aircraft will be flown with two-pilot crews.

Medium-range

Medium-range aircraft include the Boeing 757s, larger Boeing 737s, Airbus A310 and A320, McDonnell Douglas MD-80 series, and other types in the 150–200 seat passenger-capacity range. In Europe they form the mainstay of charter operations to Mediterranean destinations, though a limited transatlantic capability is an advantage. Most medium-range aircraft are for two-crew operation with no flight engineer.

Long-range

Long-range aircraft are used by some airlines remote from their principal markets. As well as the older Boeing 747SP and L1011-500 referred to, there is a strong move towards the 'Extended Range Operations' (EROPS) large-capacity twin-engined aircraft by airlines without the traffic to justify larger aircraft.

EROPS aircraft have operating standards different from others in use.

Narrow-body

Narrow-body, being the alternative to wide-body, refers either to the older types of aircraft which preceded wide-body types in an operator's fleet, or to the newer short and medium-range types bought as replacements.

Old types. Old types of narrow-body aircraft are retained because they have lower depreciation charges than newer alternatives, though this may be at the expense of higher maintenance costs and fuel consumption. Most older aircraft will not meet the new noise regulations (Stage 3/Chapter 3) being introduced in industrialised countries; this may limit their use to other countries. Operators may use their older aircraft as backup to other services.

New types. New types of narrow-body aircraft have low fuel consumption, low noise levels, low maintenance costs, and high depreciation charges. Airlines try to assign the latest equipment to the most competitive routes, and therefore availability is important. New aircraft are scheduled to achieve a high utilisation so that the capital cost may be recovered as quickly as possible. Very new aircraft may turn out to have unexpected technical problems, which the operator has to overcome with minimum disruption to service.

The operating plan

When the operating plan is devised, there are many factors to be taken into account. These will typically exist in the company as a set of objectives or planning standards which then have to be met.

Daily activity of the aircraft

For planning the day's operations, flight time and ground time allowances are needed.

Flying time and other commitments. Flight time for an aircraft and route combination is obtained by estimates from the manufacturer's performance data and from weather records, modified by company policy and experience. Short-range flight times are dominated by air traffic control considerations. For long-range flying, companies may differ in their use of fuel economy cruise techniques.

Late arrival allowance. Aircraft will not always depart and arrive on time; schedulers may provide an allowance for recovery of this lateness, especially at main bases.

Cargo loading time. Many airlines use mixed passenger—cargo loads, so that a lighter passenger load may be compensated for by carrying extra freight in under-floor holds. Cargo loading may be more common at some stations.

Towing and moving. Airport terminal capacity is often restricted or expensive. Operators have to schedule for the towing of aircraft off and onto airport departure ramps during long stays.

Standby allowance. Most airlines have some 'slack' built into their schedule to allow recovery from aircraft shortage caused by unserviceability, weather, ATC delays, or other uncertain events. The extent of this standby cover is a matter of company policy, and varies between operators and markets. In markets with several operators, it is more economical to accept occasional loss of business to a rival than to provide spare capacity which is not otherwise necessary. In charter markets more variation from plan is possible in departure times, provided the day's work gets done. In scheduled services aimed at business travellers, departure punctuality is a strong selling point which must be maintained. The extreme example of this policy is the 'shuttle' service, which has a firm promise of departure irrespective of demand, so spare aircraft have to be provided. For other services, spare aircraft are obtained by switching the planned rotations.

Disruptions to schedule

Delays along route. In long-range operations which require the sequencing of several flights by one aircraft, the possibility of a delay to one of these may have to be assumed. It is usually the case that commercial timings of departure at airports en route leave a suitable gap in the schedule.

Weather effects. Bad weather can disrupt flying for short periods. Companies may have either technical solutions (automatic landing systems fitted to aircraft) or operational solutions (alternative airports).

Maintenance needs

Unserviceability. Aircraft unserviceability has to be allowed for in the schedule planning. Ways of doing this include using the deferred-defect system in conjunction with planned routeing through maintenance bases at sufficiently regular intervals, or providing aircraft down time at stations, for work to be performed.

Scheduled maintenance. Scheduled maintenance would seem to be easier to plan for. However, it may mean making assumptions, far ahead of the event, about aircraft usage and mandatory maintenance intervals. Most operators adjust the rotation between tasks for aircraft in a fleet to achieve an average usage equivalent to the plan, in order that individual aircraft do not get out of step.

Long term plans. Long term plans are necessary to confirm that hangar capacity will be available, since planning and construction work for bases have long lead times.

Special inputs. In addition to the routine maintenance in the published schedule, the operator will have work arising from manufacturers' alerts, modifications and refurbishments.

Contingency. Aircraft damage may occur in normal use, from ground handling accidents, lightning strikes, or other non-forecastable reasons. It may also happen that a scheduled maintenance visit takes longer than planned. For these reasons contingency allowance in the form of gaps in the hangar schedule is advisable.

Marketing's perceptions

The perception of engineering by the marketing department, which is assumed to be the same as the perception of the airline by the customer, must also be taken into account. This covers several factors.

Safety

This is taken for granted. Airlines by agreement do not directly refer to safety in advertising, and the safety record of modern commercial aviation is very high. Therefore, anything which may undermine this assumption must be avoided.

Commercial changes

Alterations to aircraft for commercial reasons have high priority these days. If a major refurbishment is needed as part of a marketing campaign, then it must be fitted into the maintenance programme without delay.

Routine maintenance

The commercial department looks to the technical department to provide aircraft for its services. Failings in this will not be overlooked. The ways in which this is perceived are:

Loss of aircraft. Delivering aircraft late from maintenance checks will harm the flying programme. Removing aircraft for servicing at unplanned occasions will also have adverse effects on the standby cover which guarantees punctuality. Commercial managers will also query the need for aircraft to be out of service for technical reasons.

Effect on schedules. Aircraft which are unable to fly at the planned intensity because of unserviceability will affect the airline's revenue-earning ability. The responsibility for this will be perceived as the engineering department's, even if it is ultimately a manufacturer's deficiency.

Costs and safety

In arranging for maintenance work to be done, the scheduler has to achieve safety at minimum cost. Over-maintenance would seem at first sight to be erring on the side of caution, but experience has shown that frequently disturbing aircraft structures and systems to gain access for inspection and test is almost as likely to introduce faults as it is to find them. The scheduler will be faced with different tasks when considering scheduled maintenance or unscheduled maintenance in the short term or long term. These affect the actions taken to deal with the problem.

Scheduled maintenance

Scheduled maintenance can be programmed with a fair degree of accuracy, and therefore efficiency can be calculated. Programmes need revision because of changes in the commercial requirements or for technical reasons.

Short-term scheduled maintenance is best achieved by keeping it away from the commercial flying programme. Short routine checks can be done overnight for short-haul aircraft or on long turnrounds for long-haul. It is usual to perform these checks more frequently than required, to provide flexibility in operations if aircraft get out of position in the plan.

Long-term maintenance is planned to make maximum use of the aircraft and the maintenance facilities. Development of check intervals proceeds in conjunction with this, so that usable aircraft life is not wasted. Sometimes operators will consider bringing in an aircraft earlier than needed to get the total sequence for a fleet aligned with a best plan.

Unscheduled maintenance

Although from its definition it might seem that unscheduled maintenance cannot be planned, in practice its total volume for a fleet can be anticipated with some accuracy. This means that visits by the aircraft can be arranged at frequent enough intervals for repair to be done when necessary. Most unscheduled work on aircraft requires diagnosis of system faults and replacement of components, so the skills and equipment available should reflect this.

Short-term unscheduled maintenance can be combined with the scheduled work if enough time is available. Defects that may be deferred can thus be repaired at convenient opportunities. In some cases repair must be immediate, and if its time exceeds the aircraft turnround standard, a change of aircraft has to be made.

Long-term unscheduled maintenance may require special inputs of aircraft to maintenance bases or repair organisations. The most uncertain kind of long-term unscheduled maintenance is accident repair; sometimes the aircraft is so badly damaged that it cannot be flown back to base and a temporary workshop has to be set up away from base.

Requirements for efficient scheduled maintenance

To perform aircraft maintenance, several kinds of resources are needed. Some of these are obvious:

Plate 11 Undercarriage build workshop

Buildings and ground facilities. A place to work is necessary. In most countries, any work beyond pre-departure inspection is done under cover in a hangar. Work on engines may require ground runs to be performed, and most industrialised countries now have local legislation that prohibits this being done in the open at airports, so use of silencers or enclosures is required.

Access and parking. Aircraft not undergoing maintenance and not needed for service have to be accommodated. Airport terminals cannot provide this space, so a parking area is needed where aircraft can be put in safety at minimum cost.

Trained labour. Airworthiness regulations specify the skills and training needed for maintenance work. The operator has to make plans to obtain these.

Spares supply. Maintenance of the aircraft requires replacement of worn or defective parts, so an inventory system is needed to ensure supply of these items. Operators at large airports will be able to use manufacturers' stores on the site.

Documentation. Technical manuals must be used to describe the procedures and systems in work. All scheduled work that is planned in advance has to be described, and the unscheduled work is also entered in relevant records.

Tools and equipment. Many tasks require special tools or test equipment. The operator needs these to be available when the maintenance is to be done.

Continuity. It is normal experience in production industries that tasks performed frequently benefit from the learning effect. Therefore, a maintenance line should ideally be scheduled 'nose to tail' so that experience is accumulated. This is difficult to achieve with unscheduled maintenance, especially when shift work is used.

Maintenance-planning parameters

The operator should specify all the standards used in planning the maintenance, so that each section understands its contribution. Some examples for a large aircraft used by a major operator are:

Check level

The check cycle is broken down into a series of levels, the highest being the longest interval in time and the most extensive amount of work.

Major check. This is an interval of 18,000 aircraft airborne flying hours,

Plate 12 Boeing 747-400 wingtip

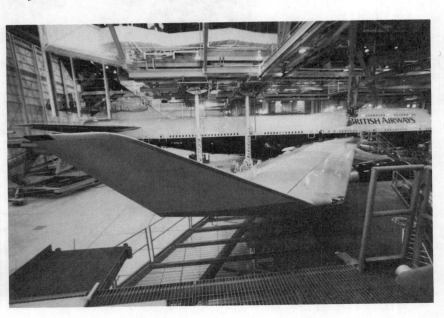

approximately every four to five years of average use. The time out of service is about 25 to 30 elapsed days, working time in hangar about 1 day less than this. This check is the most thorough stripdown that the aircraft receives, and requires all interior equipment to be removed. Repainting usually follows. Opportunity may be taken to perform major structural modifications because of this.

Inter check. Inter checks for items that cannot be scheduled for a major check interval are done every 4,500 hours and take 9 elapsed days out of service.

Service check. Service checks are done at intervals of 800 to 3,000 hours, depending on the work zone or system involved. These take from 1 to 2 elapsed days out of service and have a calendar time limit of 6 months.

Ramp check. This is done at intervals from 125 to 500 hours and takes from 3 hours elapsed time, for the most frequent checks, to 6 hours for the less frequent work.

Other checks. Various tasks such as special configurations, special inspections to certain aircraft, are fitted into the plan as required. These usually take under 5 hours elapsed time and so can be done within a normal shift.

Repainting. If not done at major checks, this is planned every 4 years. This takes about 18 days elapsed time off service for a large aircraft.

Washing. Aircraft exterior cleaning is scheduled for reasons of appearance and drag reduction.

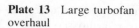

Constraints

The maintenance schedule specifies the maximum interval between various tasks. These are stated in one of several ways:

Flying hours. This is the most common, based on usage.

Landings. This is used for equipment such as landing gear or flaps, with activity proportional to flights. Pressure-cabin lives are measured in 'flight cycles', adjusted for the maximum pressure differential.

Calendar time. A maximum calendar time is sometimes specified for items, so that even if little flying is done a maintenance requirement will eventually arise. This may be a check on corrosion.

Plate 13 Large turbofan overhaul

Descheduling requirements

The time out of service should be agreed with the commercial department, and the time in work with the contractor or maintenance base.

Elapsed days/shifts/hours. For long checks, the total number of days out of service is sufficient. For shorter checks the time in shifts or hours should be stated.

Short-term unscheduled maintenance decisions

With unscheduled maintenance, it is not so easy to lay down a set of time standards. It would be better to try to specify the decision rules used in deciding when and where to repair the aircraft, for example:

Response to a problem

If a problem is revealed during operations it can be classified as either a deferred defect ('go') or one that must be repaired immediately ('no-go').

'Go' defects. A deferred defect may be repaired at the next suitable opportunity. Examples of this are to perform the work at the next station, or at the next base visit, or to send a working party out to the aircraft if it does not reach base.

'No go' defects. If the fault must be repaired at once, the first possibility to consider is to do it within the aircraft's scheduled down time. If this is adequate, there is no consequence. If it is not, then the choice is to depart late or to change the aircraft. Aircraft changes may result in passengers being inconvenienced. If the aircraft is changed, the original itself becomes subject to the same rules as for deferred defects, that is whether to repair it at base or to use a working party.

PRODUCT SUPPORT AND SPARES

Introduction

Airlines depend on aircraft manufacturers for the supply of parts, and often for the overhaul of spares. This after-sales service is usually part of a contract made at the time of purchase of the aircraft, but operators often find it difficult to ensure compliance with these contracts. The feeling that service has a lower status than manufacture in the aircraft company, and that monopoly of service discourages improvement, is common in airlines experiencing frustration at getting swift delivery or turnround of parts. In extreme cases, airlines suffering a particularly poor quality service have come to realise that full enforcement of the contract may drive the supplier out of business and leave them with no source of equipment.

Airlines are in the strongest bargaining position at the time of placing the order for a new fleet, so the temptation to negotiate a good service contract at the same time is strong. Manufacturers may be driven to make optimistic promises by the attraction of closing a sale, only to discover later that insufficient thought has been given to achieving the guaranteed high reliability, low cost, and quick delivery. In the past, many operators accused manufacturers of trying to recoup income through high prices for spares; the more sensational examples of this have been cited in the press, such as inflated charges for standard parts actually made by other suppliers, expensive tooling needed in maintenance, unnecessary modifications offered, and others.

It is difficult for the non-aeronautical person to appreciate these arguments because almost everything concerned with aircraft is very expensive as a result of the design and certification requirements. A complete aircraft costs tens of millions of dollars, engines cost millions of dollars, turbine blades or vanes can cost thousands of dollars each, fasteners can cost many times the equivalent part used in ground-based machinery.

Plate 14 Mechanical
workshop

Inventory costs

All airlines are now turning their attention to reducing inventory costs by minimising stocks of spare parts held. Once, it was common to estimate how many spares would be needed over the life of the aircraft and to buy them with the aircraft, for a cost of up to 15 per cent of the new aircraft price. As the expense of doing this increased, buying parts in instalments after fleet delivery was tried. This relies on the fact that some maintenance is not needed in the early years of an aircraft's use, and also allows for some adjustment to purchases after experience of their actual usage rates. This scheme fails if the aircraft's sales are so poor that the equipment suppliers curtail their investment in it.

More recently, operators have begun to require manufacturers to assume more responsibility for reliability and cost of parts in these early years of use. Three-year fixed-price contracts, during which the actual economic performance will be established before transfer to the operator, are not uncommon.

Spares pools operated by IATA are another example which has now been in use for a long time. European maintenance consortia, such as ATLAS and KSSU, are another way of reducing support costs. US carriers have not followed the same solution, partly because attempts to form industry-wide common spares holdings were discouraged by the regulatory authority on anti-trust legislation grounds, and also because larger US airlines have the economy of scale not possessed by European operators. The US industry has also had a longer tradition of maintenance-only organisations, so that operators have been able to rely on independent servicing of their equipment.

In the United States, the Air Transport Association (ATA) has set up ATA Specification 2000, as a database of aircraft parts available online to operators. This gives details in a standard format, and will eventually enable paperless transactions to be conducted. ATA also has a project called Airline Inventory Redistribution System (AIRS), which lists parts surplus to a carrier's needs. Airlines could use this to dispose of unused parts if a buyer is found.

Other solutions proposed for the airline-spares inventory problems are:

— selective provisioning for different shortage risks;
— better forecasting models;
— more use of real-time computer systems;
— 'just-in-time' policies;
— manufacturer's spares depots.

Aircraft spares in British Airways

British Airways' engineering inventory is valued at about £375M; for comparison the airline's total annual operating expenditure under all headings is about £4,000M. The main inventory categories are expendable (used once and then discarded) or rotable (may be restored by repair); there are further divisions within these categories. Rotables may have serial numbers which enable the actual part to be identified physically and recorded in a computer system.

Processing of spares

An operator will have at least one warehouse to handle all spares and material for the company, both ingoing and outgoing items. The central receipt and despatch area has to deal with various kinds of inventory items which may be:

— expendable;
— rotable;
— contracts;
— loans;
— new purchases.

All of this must be checked for compliance with quality-control requirements, in addition to the normal business activity of any engineering company. Most operators use computer-based stock control systems to manage their spares and material, but the systems used by airlines may differ from those common in other production or distribution industries. One reason for this is the large number of distinct parts involved in aircraft maintenance work. Another important reason is the requirement for a maintenance or ownership history of the parts to be kept.

Spares pools are operated by users of common aircraft types. These reduce the need for every operator to locate spares at stations away from the main base. In the pool, each operator is designated as the major supplier at his base, and if another operator needs a spare at that station it is borrowed to get the aircraft back to its main base — the loan unit is returned as soon as practically possible to its owner. In this way the cost of spares to each operator is reduced.

Contract repairs are arranged because even large operators may not find it economic or practical to fully maintain all their spares. Work is exchanged between operators on a commercial basis, or with specialist repair organisations and manufacturers who provide support. For new aircraft types, it is common for the operator to contract component repair and overhaul to the vendor during the early years, with some form of incentive contracting to promote cost savings and reliability improvements.

Requirements for control

There are two sets of requirements for inventory control. These are the Airworthiness regulations and company policies.

The UK CAA Airworthiness Notice No. 11 covers acceptance of aircraft parts for civil operators. This is a short note pending issue of a formal British Civil Airworthiness Requirement (BCAR). BCAR Section A defines the responsibilities of those accepting aeronautical parts for incorporation into an aircraft or its equipment, and of those placing sub-contract orders with companies that do not hold CAA approval. It thus applies to manufacturers or operators. Detailed procedures for

Plate 15 Stock control data collection

operators to follow are not given here; other CAA documents give information for operators.

Aeronautical parts here are defined with respect to airworthiness, not for inventory control or other reasons. The user is responsible for ensuring that the parts are serviceable and conform to the standard for the intended application. This implies that both parties have access to relevant parts catalogues and test or process standards. Beyond this, approved repair or overhaul documentation must exist for organisations to use.

The CAA defines three primary parameters for achieving airworthiness; these are the performance, reliability/maintainability and life of the part. Specifications should define materials and construction required for continued satisfactory performance. Variations to this build standard are only permissible if concession or modification action has been agreed with the appropriate design organisation.

Although all manufacturers or overhaul organisations must have their own quality-control systems, the CAA document puts the final onus on the user to confirm that the parts are correct. The Notice explains this more fully, to avoid misunderstandings.

Basic rules for purchasing parts and verifying receipt are also given in the Notice. These include periodic confidence checks on suppliers, documentation checks, and visits to suppliers for confirmation of procedures followed. It is thus apparent that the user is expected to take an active role in ensuring that adequate quality standards are met by supplying organisations, and not merely to limit his work to scrutiny of incoming material and documents.

The sale and purchase of used or surplus spares by airlines is becoming more common, with the growing pressure on reducing inventory levels to the minimum needed for current fleet operations. Thus an operator who is downgrading the utilisation of an older aircraft type, perhaps to less popular routes, will want to dispose of some spares, perhaps to a charter operator who still uses the type intensively. An issue that has become important in these dealings is 'traceability', which means the recorded maintenance history of all parts in the sale. Responsible operators must be able to satisfy airworthiness authorities that they know the state of their spares. There have been a few accidents to aircraft caused by use of non-authorised parts with poor quality control.

MAINTENANCE SHARING

European examples

One solution to the high cost of the facilities and staff needed for modern aircraft maintenance is the inter-airline maintenance sharing agreement. The best known examples of this in Europe are the two groups ATLAS and KSSU. ATLAS consists of Air France, Alitalia, Iberia, Lufthansa and Sabena. KSSU consists of KLM, SAS, Swissair and UTA. It is not clear yet what effect the Air France takeover of UTA will have on this.

These consortia were formed originally to support wide-body jets in the 1970s. Agreement on cockpit layouts, to standardise on training, was reached before purchase of the aircraft, in the case of the DC10 in ATLAS. Other equipment normally specified by customers is also specified in common, so that the full benefit of combined spares holding and work-sharing can be obtained. This means that about three-quarters of the major spares (rotables) are common to the group.

The allocation of maintenance is such that, within each group, one partner is the main provider of airframe major-check maintenance for one aircraft type, another of engine overhaul to one engine model or manufacturer, another of mechanical or electrical component repair and overhaul, and so on. This leads to a few cases where a partner is doing work for an aircraft that is not in his fleet. It produces significant savings in hangar and workshop construction, since major aircraft checks need special equipment for access, and engines need expensive test houses. Movement of aircraft and parts between different bases is not a great problem; most of the sites are less than 1000 km apart, and scheduled intervals between checks, or average times between engine removals, are fairly lengthy.

Other examples

Although successful in Europe, this idea has not been much used in other parts of the world. Reasons for this may be:

— anti-trust legislation (in the USA);
— economic instability and fluctuating exchange rates or exchange controls;
— customs-clearance problems and other cross-border obstacles;

The US Foreign Repair Stations Act

— geographical separation between partners;
— skill differences between partners.

One example often quoted of a group that failed is East African Airways, once a Joint Venture between Kenya, Tanzania and Uganda. Kenya became the dominant member as growth expectations for the others were not realised. Foreign-exchange transactions and delays in payments led to the breakdown of the group. A region that met most of the requirements for such a group was the Eastern Europe Comecon bloc, though no attempt was made to form one, perhaps for political reasons.

THE US FOREIGN REPAIR STATIONS ACT

This is an example of the kind of political problem which can frustrate maintenance organisations in their attempts to find the best source of work.

History

In 1952, the US Federal Aviation Administration (FAA) imposed a rule on US airlines banning the use of so-called 'foreign repair stations', or non-US maintenance organisations. This was the Federal Aviation Regulations (FAR) Part 145, preventing US carriers from using such sources for aircraft operated entirely in the US.

Conflict

In 1987 the FAA published a proposal to relax this restriction, but reaction to it from US industry was hostile, even though counter-reaction from other nations, such as from European operators, was also voiced.

The FAA had tried to emphasise the existing rule more strongly in 1986, as commercial pressures caused by the post-1978 US deregulation made operators anxious to seek cheaper maintenance abroad. High wages and fringe benefits, achieved by US airline unions in the engineering and flight operations departments of US airlines during the relatively well protected era of licensed competition, were believed to be one of the strong reasons for some legislators favouring deregulation. Deregulation introduced a demand for the smaller commuter aircraft as cross-subsidy of routes by major operators was abandoned. These aircraft were largely overseas in origin, and domestic maintenance, instead of repair by the manufacturer, was not always immediately available.

Overseas maintenance contractors, expecting orders for support of these products, were of course highly dissatisfied with this decision. Protectionism had become an issue in US politics for other home industries, such as automobiles, consumer electronics and even larger transport aircraft, facing what was regarded as unfair foreign competition. Lobbyists campaigned against any further deterioration of US industrial markets in this way. Threats of trade wars between the nations were made.

The FAA argument for this sudden stiffening of its rules was that its attention had been distracted in the early 1980s by other matters, including the effects of attempts to decrease government spending by reducing staff. A survey conducted by the FAA in 1984 showed some operators using foreign maintenance in contradiction of established rules, and an accident in 1985, to a US operated aircraft, revealed more evidence of overseas overhauled parts. The FAA felt that its existing rules were being flouted, and therefore issued a reminder of them. This provoked an adverse reaction from those who regarded the FAA's previous silence as tacit acceptance of the situation.

Resolution

The new proposal, 'Revision of Foreign Repair Station Rules', allowed any certificated facility to perform work on any US aircraft or component. Since many overseas organisations were already FAA approved, this was welcomed by them. Objections came from the domestic US trade unions. The US Congress was pressed into making funds dependent on this change being dropped, though the immediate effect was only to postpone it for a year. Other schemes devised in these negotiations included allowing foreign manufacturers to work on their own equipment, but withdrawing approval for overseas bases supervised by a US airline. Larger US airlines interested in global expansion saw the establishment of overseas bases as a necessary part of this strategy, making them more acceptable to foreign governments as potential employers.

The European Community issued a joint protest at these restrictions, citing the acknowledged admission of its proponents that air safety was not an issue, and quoting the GATT Agreement on Civil Aircraft in support of their views. The use of 'safety' as a device to aid protectionist legislation is familiar to observers of European trade politics. US–European air transport relations were already strained by the conduct of bilateral route negotiations after US deregulation and by attempts to obtain a fair code of practice for use of computer reservation systems.

The result was a European proposal to enact a contrary law banning the servicing of European-registered aircraft in the USA. Many European operators used US companies because the volume of business did not make it economic for them to set up their own repair workshops. European airlines spent more in the USA on maintenance than the US airlines spent in Europe, and the 1986 edict had affected some European companies badly. Other European aircraft-industry trade associations protested to the US government. Other consequences of the FAA prohibition were legal difficulties in confirming airworthiness of aircraft and parts, causing loss of asset value as well as loss of business.

In 1989, the FAA revised its policy to meet the demands for worldwide maintenance of US-registered aircraft. In the new rules, US airlines would be able to obtain repair and maintenance from FAA-certificated foreign repair stations. The limitation to aircraft used in whole or in part outside the USA was removed, and the permission was extended to include engines and components.

AIRCRAFT MAINTENANCE IN THE RAF

Civil and military differences

Aircraft maintenance in a military organisation differs from that of a civil operator in a number of ways, some of which are:

The aircraft flying rate. The utilisation of military combat aircraft is typically a few hundred flying hours per year; compare this with civil airliners which are expected to achieve up to 4,000 flying hours per aircraft per year. This arises from the different functions of the operator. The military requirement in peacetime is to meet training objectives whilst maintaining the aircraft ready for war. The civil need is to earn profit from the aircraft as soon as possible.

Structural stresses. Modern emphasis on low-level flying practice for military operations increases structural stresses, and also introduces a higher risk of ingestion damage or erosion. Civil duty cycles are typically once per flight, most aircraft cruise at high altitude where turbulence is less than at low level. RAF experience is that fatigue-related modifications may be needed after a few years of service with some aircraft types. Civil experience is usually that fatigue is a high-time related problem. Both operators experience corrosion problems which are related to aircraft age and operating environment.

The number of bases. Military operations must be conducted from a number of bases capable if necessary of being self-sufficient in war, although third line maintenance is usually centralised. Civil operators typically centralise all major maintenance at one base and use line stations for servicing needed only to support the flying.

Size of aircraft. Many military aircraft are 'fast jets' of single or two-seat crew, and are small in size. The inevitable outcome of this is limited access for technical tradesmen during maintenance, so intensive maintenance programmes can be difficult to plan.

Age of aircraft. Some military aircraft are now retained in service much longer than would be considered economic to maintain by a civil operator. This may happen because of a change in plans forced by circumstances, such as the cancellation of the AEW Nimrod project, or because a more cost-effective alternative to the in-service aircraft cannot be readily obtained.

Unusual skills required of personnel, such as ability to perform emergency battle-damage repairs, or requirement to practise servicing in special protective clothing and be ready to deploy to remote sites.

The methods of financing and budgeting have many differences from the civil way, but also growing similarities.

Military examples

RAF aircraft have a different scheduled maintenance cycle from that of civil ones. Scheduled major maintenance occurs about once every 5 to 6 years; the content of a scheduled major is about 10,000 to 20,000 manhours, depending on the aircraft type. Down time is usually several months (50–100 working days). The total effort on a modern aircraft type is about 50 per cent scheduled work, 30 per cent unscheduled, 20 per cent modifications. The experience is for manhours per major check to increase with years in service; this has to be arrested or reduced by paying special attention to problems that are seen, by developing better repair schemes or modifications to improve reliability.

The RAF estimate that total cost of maintenance for an aircraft type is about 2 to 3 times its initial purchase price; potentially, therefore, there are considerable savings in defence costs to be made in maintenance. The greatest benefit is obtained by using a reliability assurance programme before entry to service; this is cheaper than doing it afterwards. Future policy, for aircraft such as the EFA, is for the manufacturer to have responsibility for maintenance support in the initial years of service.

RAF maintenance definitions

The RAF maintenance policy for an item is described by a standard terminology defined in Air Publications 100A-01 and which indicates the location, depth, and routeing of the item from removal to repair. These are determined by maintenance studies before introduction of the aircraft into service, and are periodically reviewed during the life of the aircraft, in the light of experience.

Location of work

First line. The maintenance organisation immediately responsible for the maintenance and preparation for use of the complete systems or equipment. First line organisations normally undertake Depth A maintenance but may be authorised to undertake some Depth B maintenance.

Second line. The maintenance organisation responsible for providing maintenance support to specified first line organisations. Second line organisations normally undertake Depth B maintenance but may be authorised to undertake some Depth C maintenance.

Third line. The maintenance organisation within the Services but excluding the organisations within first and second line. Third line organisations, although able to undertake all depths of maintenance, normally undertake Depths C and D maintenance.

Fourth line. The industrial maintenance organisation providing maintenance support beyond second line, to the Services, under contract. Fourth line organisations, although able to undertake all depths of maintenance, normally undertake Depths C and D maintenance.

Depth of maintenance

Depth A. That maintenance which is directly concerned with preparing end items for use, and keeping them in day-to-day order. It may include such operations as functional testing, replenishment, servicing, re-arming, role changing, minor modification, fault diagnosis, and corrective maintenance by replacement, adjustment or minor repair.

Depth B. That maintenance which is required on items and assemblies which are in an unacceptable condition or which require preventive maintenance. This may include scheduled maintenance, embodiment of prescribed modifications, bay maintenance of assemblies, and corrective maintenance beyond Depth A but within generally provisioned resources.

Depth C. That maintenance which is the repair, partial reconditioning and modification requiring special skills, special equipment or relatively infrequently used capability which is not economic to provide generally, but which is short of complete strip, reconditioning and re-assembly.

Depth D. That maintenance which is full reconditioning, major conversion or such major repair that involves work of this depth.

Other terms

Other definitions used are:

Operating system. Any aircraft or ground simulator in which the LRU or module is installed, and which may be included in the maintenance policy.

Line Replaceable Unit (LRU). Any item which can be removed at first line.

Module/Shop Replacement Unit (SRU). The next level of exchange in a LRU.

Component. A piece part, detail part, or consumable item required for the maintenance of a LRU or module. A LRU may contain no module/SRU, in which case the next level in it is a component.

Arising rate. The rate at which a LRU or module is removed from its operating system and enters the maintenance cycle.

Filter bench (FB). A method, using standard serviceability tests, for confirming the serviceability of a LRU or module. This can avoid the need for further unnecessary maintenance on items found to be serviceable.

Fillrate. The probability that a demand for a spare is met immediately, with no delay in response.

Backorder. Action taken when the number of demands for a spare exceeds the number of serviceable spares available. A measure of unsatisfied demand.

Examples of use

Examples of maintenance policy are:

1A-4D, which means that the LRU is first removed at first line and then sent to a maintenance organisation for full reconditioning.

1A-2B-4D is similar except for a possible intervening module/SRU change at second line.

1A-2B/REG/FB-4 means that the LRU is removed at first line, sent to a regional second line facility where a filter bench is used, where the unserviceable LRU is maintained down to module/SRU level if possible, otherwise it is sent to a maintenance organisation.

RAF St Athan

RAF St Athan is a major third-line maintenance unit, responsible for airframe, engine, and mechanical repairs and overhauls on RAF aircraft. Among the aircraft serviced there is the Tornado, its engines and many components. The workforce includes Service personnel, local civilians, and manufacturers' working parties on some modification tasks.

Overhaul work

Major overhaul of a Tornado takes about 13,400 manhours and is scheduled for shift working at 72 working days. The peak workload, for maintenance and fatigue modification, expected to be reached in the financial year 1991/92, will occupy 30 tracks and use shift working to increase utilisation of the facilities. Major maintenance on the aircraft involves removal of most components and strip down to the primary structure, so that inspection and modification can be accomplished.

Maintenance of the mechanical components on this and many other RAF aircraft is also done at St Athan. Avionic and electrical components are maintained at another maintenance unit, RAF Sealand. Component repair and overhaul is not automatically done by these RAF units; manufacturers and independent maintenance organisations are also considered for the work, on a contract basis. Among the reasons cited for performing work in-house are:

— quicker turnround of parts, thus reducing spares holdings and aircraft unserviceability;
— lower cost of repairs made by locally devised schemes;
— better utilisation of facilities and specialist labour.

The framework for this is provided by the Executive Responsibility Budget, introduced by the Ministry of Defence some years ago. This makes units accountable for their costs and includes transfer charging to and from other units, as well as between the RAF and outside contractors as before. Its intention was for units to become more aware of their costs and thus to seek improvements in efficiency by their own actions.

No. 30 Maintenance Unit — RAF Sealand

No. 30 Maintenance Unit is the largest avionic repair facility in Europe. It repairs avionic units for RAF aircraft and some other contracts, with a range of several thousand product lines. This covers technology from microwave integrated circuits and digital systems, to valve technology of the 1950s. Its responsibility includes many kinds of airborne instrument and control equipment, so electromechanical instruments and air data computers used in the 1960s have to be supported, as well as later analogue or digital equipment. Many systems have significant mechanical components, such as the radar steering device on older aircraft, so the Unit's expertise extends beyond electrical, radio, and electronic skills.

Exchange scheme

This service is performed by the Avionic Direct Exchange Scheme (ADES), which guarantees delivery to a specified performance target for any unit requested. This scheme operates as follows:

Each week every flying unit informs 30MU, by signal or through the USAS supply computer system, of the avionic items it requires; these are components which cannot be maintained at the local unit.

The ADES computer allocates available serviceable components to customers and calculates which extra components must be produced in that week to meet these demands. A weekly production schedule is then printed for the workshops.

The workshops then bring forward repairable components for the schedule, and work to produce the items needed to meet that week's demands and to replenish the serviceable stocks, whose holding level is based on longer-term experience of average demand for that item. The workshop production target is that 90 per cent of each week's demands must be satisfied on the first week following delivery. Serviceable components are packed in locally-produced special containers and made up into pallet loads. These pallets are then loaded into a vehicle being routed to the appropriate destination. 30MU has its own fleet of dedicated delivery vehicles, capable of protecting the delicate equipment en route, and runs a route network taking in all major flying units in Britain and RAF Germany. At the destination unit, the pallets of serviceable items are quickly exchanged for the unserviceable items from the flying unit.

The unserviceable items are returned to 30MU and enter the start of the workshop repair cycle.

AIRCRAFT WEIGHT CONTROL

Weight control in airlines

Operators are required to weigh their aircraft at regular intervals. This is specified in British Civil Airworthiness Requirements (BCAR) Chapter A5-4 Part 3.1.1, for aircraft over 5,700 kg maximum weight, as initially within two years of manufacture and then at least every five years. The intervals are given in the maintenance schedule so that plans to weigh each aircraft can be made. An obvious requirement is a suitably large weighbridge; a major operator will have one of these.

The experience of most operators is that aircraft weight increases with age, owing to repairs, modifications, and unaccounted alterations. Engineering staff keep records of known changes and their estimated weight effects, but it is often the case that a value quoted for work is a synthetic estimate and actual weighing of all the parts is difficult or impossible. It is also an unfortunate experience that new aircraft can turn out to weigh more than the intended specification, because of late changes in customer equipment, changes by suppliers or engineering changes agreed by the customer.

A good practice is to keep a total of the calculated weight change, and to request a check weighing if this exceeds a threshold value. Examples of these limits are shown in Table 4.2. It can be seen that these are very small tolerances.

In addition to control of the weight, measurement of the aircraft's centre of gravity is also necessary.

Weights

Basic Weight is that of the aircraft and its essential equipment, including any unusable fuel and oil remaining in the tanks of an operational aircraft. This should correspond to the calculated weight estimated by the operator from maintenance records.

Operating Empty Weight equals the Basic Weight plus that of the crew and their effects, plus removable catering and containers used for baggage, freight (unit load devices, ULDs).

Table 4.2 Aircraft weight limits

Aircraft	Limit	MTOW	Limit as % of MTOW
Boeing 747	200 kg	378,000 kg	0.05
Boeing 737	100 kg	56,500 kg	0.20
BAe 748	25 kg	21,000 kg	0.10

Maximum Zero Fuel Weight is a structural limit applied by the aircraft designers, taking into account the bending relief offered by the fuel load which is normally carried in the wing tanks (some aircraft have tail tanks).

Maximum Landing Weight is also specified by the aircraft designers and is related to the airframe strength and the shock-absorbing capacity of the undercarriage. If an impact exceeds the limits set by this, a witness mark will be left on an external indicator fixed to the undercarriage main oleo leg; it may also show on the flight data recorder trace. Obviously, such an event will result in a special inspection to assess any damage suffered.

Maximum Take-off Weight is related to the structural strength and airfield performance required.

Maximum Ramp Weight includes an allowance for fuel burnt during taxying from terminal to runway.

Payload

Payload is determined by the difference between the maximum weight and the empty weight. Most aircraft are designed so that the maximum payload possible for purely structural reasons is greater than the payload allowable when a full fuel load is carried. This means that, when the desired range, and therefore fuel load, is increased for a particular aircraft, then beyond a certain point payload has to be reduced to keep within the maximum take-off limit. Therefore weight growth can have an adverse effect on revenue-earning ability if it is known and allowed for in advance, or a serious effect on operational safety if it is not accounted for. (Loading errors have been at least a contributory factor in some take-off accidents.)

Weight change

During the life of the aircraft, weight changes may occur to much of the removable equipment, either upwards as a result of increases in requirements (higher cabin-service standards, mandatory safety requirements, environmental legislation, etc.) or downwards as a result of technical improvements (lighter materials and construction). Examples of necessary changes affecting aircraft weight were the fire safety improvements and engine-noise reductions required during the 1980s; aircraft built and delivered in the 1970s had to be modified to comply with these regulations in order to continue in operation.

Operators may also undertake maintenance programmes with the specific intention of reducing weight; this usually happens when fuel prices rise, since savings in weight are expected to benefit fuel consumption. Regular checks are thus important to keep track of the actual aircraft weight. Over the 20-year life of an aircraft, weight growth can amount to 4 per cent of basic weight. In some cases an operator will deliberately seek out the lightest aircraft in a fleet for scheduling on those routes where payload—range limitations are the most critical (westbound long-range trips).

Reduction of cockpit crew, with the trend to two-pilot operation in 'glass cockpits', is useful, but is probably not the principal reason for doing this, crew salaries being higher than the cost of weight saved. Reduction of cabin staff numbers is not possible for legal reasons, though weight control of cabin staff appears to be practised by some airlines, and is a contentious issue in labour relations. Again, the main reason for this is probably not economic. (One airline quoted a value of about $100 per kg for the weight-saving of cabin crew.)

Cost of weight

One indirect way of exercising control of weight is to place a cost on it, to be used in all evaluations involving a potential weight change. Most operators have given a lot of thought to this at various times, but the figures produced can vary widely. For instance several different studies in one airline gave the results shown in Table 4.3.

Table 4.3 Estimated cost of weight changes

Aircraft	Cost of weight (£/kg/aircraft/year)		
	Study 1	*Study 2*	*Study 3*
Type A	£97	£46	£15
Type B	£137	£57	£34

Fuel prices were highest for study 1 and lowest for study 3.

Estimates like these were originally based on averages for such factors as payload, revenue and prices. With the wider availability of data, and calculations on computers, more refined investigations and more frequent revisions are possible. However, such detailed studies usually reveal that most of the cost is incurred on a few routes with a few aircraft at selected dates, so the results should be reviewed frequently.

BUDGETARY CONTROL

Introduction

In business, particularly where competition sets prices, effective use of resources and control of costs are essential to profits and survival. Control means communication about plans, motivation of people to perform work, and measurement of performance. The process must recognise the responsibility of managers and provide them with the tools to achieve this. Business organisation nowadays functions by dividing the company into cost centres for accounting and reporting purposes. These centres often correspond to physical areas such as workshops, hangars, or servicing centres in aircraft maintenance, but they can also apply to staff functions such as quality control, information technology, and safety groups.

Control

Budgetary control is one important part of the planning process. In a modern business, budgets are made to support requests for manpower, materials, and capital equipment needed to carry out the work specified in the operating plan. In an airline it is vital to be able to relate these to the anticipated volume of output measured in aircraft hours, because sudden unexpected changes in demand may occur as a result of economic or political forces in other regions of the world. Diverting production to other parts of the world as a response to disappointment in one area is not always possible in the air transport industry.

Operating budgets are usually tied to the financial year, and accountants then collate them, together with an estimate of total revenue, to forecast profitability. This often means that several attempts at establishing a budget for the forthcoming year are needed to obtain a satisfactory result. Once set, the budget for a manager or section is used to monitor expenditure and to decide action if deviations from the plan arise. Items such as significant capital expenditure on new buildings require longer time-scales and are treated separately.

Other controls

Although budgeting as described in accounting texts is largely concerned with measurements in money, it may include performance statements about quality of service, such as on-time delivery, average turnround times, or other non-monetary events. In theory these can be costed with the aid of further research, but the arguments over attributing charges can be difficult to follow, and many senior managers prefer single-figure targets which everyone in the organisation can understand. Examples are the late delivery of aircraft after maintenance checks, the proportion of spare-parts demands met by a workshop within one week, and the percentage of departures delayed for engineering reasons attributed to different aircraft systems. Some of these are intended to act as checks on the financial targets — a workshop could achieve lower costs by arranging incoming work into batches, but this would adversely affect the supply reliability; a hangar manager could overspend on resources to guarantee early finishes, but this would increase operating costs.

Planning is based on agreed standards for times and costs of routine tasks, derived from historical records. However, management often wishes to see improvements in certain areas, so a process of negotiation over acceptable targets may take place. Introduction of new working practices might change some job times, purchase of new equipment may alter some processes. In the absence of hard estimates or outside experience on the effects of changes, an internal technical specialist may be asked to 'volunteer' a claim for the improvement in the standard. In this way, a development engineer could give an estimate for the effect of a modification on failure rate or material cost. This is inevitably rather subjective, but helps to commit people to realising the objective.

CHAPTER 5 COMPUTER SYSTEMS

COMPUTERS IN AIRCRAFT MAINTENANCE

Introduction

Industry has come to depend on computers for information storage, processing and retrieval. This is different from the original purpose of computers, which was to assist scientists in calculation. Thus developments in computational power have had to be matched by increases in storage capacity and transmission speed for business users interested in real-time information systems such as airline seat reservation control.

Other uses of computers that have grown rapidly in the last ten years are the interactive tasks like word processing, computer-aided design (CAD) — which usually means just the drafting, not the actual design calculations as an aircraft engineer might understand it. One of the consequences of this trend is that a large share of the computer processing is occupied with continuously managing the graphical display, which has made it difficult to adapt these requirements to terminals and networks designed in an age when text-only displays were thought to be adequate.

A side effect of these trends is that computer hardware prices fall steadily for equivalent performance, but software costs rise unless their development can be spread over larger numbers of sales. This has meant that standard programs for widely used tasks have maintained their price, but specialist programs requiring labour-intensive development are expensive. In business use, so-called 'fourth generation' software, which allows development of some programs adapted to special needs, usually database applications, has appeared to deal with these problems. Artificial intelligence languages are sometimes referred to as 'fifth generation', implying that they are even more versatile. Automatic translators, simulations, even calculators, can be written in these languages but their impact on most software development has so far been limited. One reason is the need to obtain a base of facts and rules to start with, another labour-intensive process.

History

Most airlines have used computer systems as part of their aircraft maintenance activity for many years. Business computers first appeared in the 1950s and were taken up by the larger companies who could afford to buy the costly equipment and hire the scarce talents needed to use it, and could see the potential benefits of applying automation to data processing. As computer power increased steadily and software became more plentiful, more companies began to use computers.

The early applications of computers in maintenance were limited to the standard business functions of payroll, purchase inventory and other accounting systems. The first distinctive use of computers in airlines was in airline seat reservation control and ticketing sales, because the economic gains from automating these functions were expected to be very great.

In the 1960s, larger airlines began applying computer systems to specialised aircraft-maintenance functions. The method used to keep track of component ages and lives on aircraft was an obvious target for this, since 'hard-time' control was common then and it was a mandatory requirement to schedule component removals from the aircraft for subsequent overhaul. Systems using punched cards were already in use, and transfer to an electronic computer was possible without extensive redesign of the information flow. A by-product of the computer recording was the availability of statistical analysis to aid in better estimation of component lives. These systems only recorded items installed on the aircraft; after removal the components became 'invisible' to the computer. The next logical step was to implement a method of tracking components through the repair circuit. This usually took much longer to implement than the first phase, for a number of reasons:

— Component recording on aircraft was a well-defined requirement, for legal reasons.
— A fairly uniform system was applied to all components on the aircraft, from simple fittings up to an entire engine.
— Control of the aircraft-fitted components was almost entirely within the operator's organisation.

Implementation of the inventory-control system had to contend with many problems:

— Agreement on the basic data, its collection and reporting had to be obtained. Some users expected far too much of a computer system, and failed to appreciate the need for accurate data.
— Operators often used different control systems, appropriate to the cost of items involved, in the same organisation. Thus high-cost rotable components had a more intricate manual control system than low-cost repairables or consumables.
— The system had to deal with internal work and with external contracted work. Often the only data available for outside items were estimates, whose inaccuracy became apparent once attempts were made to use the system for control purposes.

Experience

A number of problems common to both systems were also encountered:

— The large variety of inventory items in aircraft maintenance; consultants hired from other industries found it hard to adjust to the sheer volume of data required.
— High turnover of computer specialists; this could be faster than the completion time of a major project, with the result that incoming successors started by redesigning the system.
— Excessive reliance on batch processing of data and standard printed reports. This had worked well with the original accounting type of application, where information needed was familiar to the users, but in the specialised maintenance systems users frequently found it hard to locate information in printouts.

The consequence of these problems was that development of inventory control systems went through several phases before being suitable for integration with the rest of the engineering activity.

Planning functions

None of these early computer systems performed any planning function, except for the ability to forecast scheduled component removals by feeding the system with a projected set of aircraft ages over the future period. In the era before the personal computer, work planning was still done by multiplying ratios (manhours per flying hour) and volumes (total flying hours); this was not a very accurate process, and variations of actual to budget workload could be large. The existence of a data bank in different computer systems — removal rates in the component control section, manhours in the management accounting system, and so on — did prompt some users to try implementing what is now known as material resource planning (MRP): multiplying and adding everything at the lowest level of recorded detail inside the computer and so obtaining the total. Most early systems suffered from slow response and inadequate data. Entering large amounts of data manually was tedious, either requiring clerical staff to key it in from existing paperwork, or expecting workshop staff to enter data from a visual display unit (VDU) terminal. Systems analysts quickly came to realise that any feature of the system provided to handle exceptions was misused if users found it speeded up a transaction. Thus in one system users discovered that it was easier to create a fake new part and its number than to undergo the entry checking involved in accepting a real part, with the inevitable result that the computer became clogged with useless data. Those devising defect reporting and manhour or material recording systems became weary of seeing the largest category reported as 'miscellaneous'.

On the other hand, development, quality and planning engineers who took an active interest in the system and its use were rewarded with a much better insight into the consequences of their actions than before. Decisions on when and where to service components could be made with more confidence, and surplus capacity identified with more ease than before. Isolation of high-cost items suitable for engineering action became a routine task, and the accumulation of measured experience gave operators a useful bargaining point in negotiations with suppliers of future equipment.

Following the introduction of maintenance-event recording systems, attention turned to planning and control by computer. Apart from the desire to automate a tedious manual task, the interest lay in using the computer to explore alternatives and to search for an optimum solution. For instance, before computers were introduced, workload planning for ramp servicing generated by the flying schedule was done only for one assumed peak day in the year; what happened elsewhere could not be investigated by the office staff available. A more serious defect was that effects of disturbance to the schedule could not be studied, and it was well known that a peak-period schedule could suffer extensive disruption if events did not go according to plan.

Optimisation

Projects using computer simulation methods were developed to assist in these tasks, with varying degrees of success. These generated even greater demands for data in the form of probability distributions of elapsed times, decision rules for handling events, and interpretation of the output. Operations research models of this kind depend on the interest of management for their success; if managers are not accustomed to thinking and deciding quantitatively and logically, no amount of computer processing will remedy this.

It must be admitted that some management decisions expressed numerically are arrived at in an arbitrary way, however. Thus one may choose a delay rate of 9 per cent just because it is a 'single figure', and target on-time delivery rates of 95 per cent or 99 per cent are common without much analytical backing. Labour utilisation rates are often decided by a feeling of what the workforce is capable of rather than a complete optimisation — given the very high cost of aircraft and spares, it may be economic always to have men waiting for aircraft, but this affects morale and skills adversely.

Networking

The most recent developments in computer use take advantage of the rapid processing power and networking provided by modern systems. Thus interactive use of terminals is replacing examination of batch processed reports, and local calculation in a personal computer on data extracted from a central store is used for planning. Operators see considerable advantage in networking of computers, and some advanced uses are being studied. Among the consequences foreseen for networking a company activity are:

— The disappearance of the traditional office, which is based on the paperwork flow.
— Reduction in the levels of management and supervision, since these are traditionally associated with paper information systems.
— Transition to a 'flat' organisation structure, separated by specialisation and function rather than by hierarchy.
— Elimination of paper; this is one prediction for computers that has so far failed to reach expectations. However, with graphical displays and large capacity storage media now becoming common and cheap, this may at last happen.

MAINTENANCE COMPUTER SYSTEMS IN BRITISH AIRWAYS

Examples of use

Computers in British Airways are used to process maintenance data for many purposes, some notable examples being:

Aircraft technical log entry database. This system, defect information and serviceability control (DISC), contains all the information entered as legal requirement in the log for every flight, including the pilot's reports and ground engineer's response. Online access to this data is provided by terminals in maintenance control, hangars and technical services offices, so that an analysis of aircraft defects and repairs can be obtained by using search commands for any criteria and sequence needed — by aircraft, fleet, component, station, and so on. Before this, such analysis had to be done manually through the paper second copies of technical logs kept at the maintenance base.

Component tracking. This system, total inventory management for engineering (TIME), integrates previous maintenance recording and inventory control systems which functioned separately, one for those components installed on aircraft, and the other for components in the repair/overhaul circuit. The ambition to link up these two and thus to provide a complete component tracking system which enabled the status of an item to be established wherever it was located was achieved. TIME at present does not extend beyond the airline into subcontractors; improving this area is the next objective.

Data entry

Much of the data required for these computer systems is still entered manually, though wherever possible use of devices such as bar-coding and employee badges is made in order to reduce tiresome keying of routine data. In future, more of the essential data about aircraft operations will be supplied by the international aircraft communication and reporting system (ACARS). This system, already used in the USA, will enable advance notice of aircraft defects to be transmitted automatically to ground stations for onward transmission to maintenance bases. Maintenance staff will thus be able to respond more quickly to technical problems by having staff and equipment ready when the aircraft arrives, or by making a decision to defer the rectification of the defect to a future date.

Information strategy

The effective use of information is now regarded as an important contribution to the competitive advantage of the airline, and this is reflected in the strategic information

systems plan (SISP). Savings anticipated in five years almost amount to the equivalent of the cost of five wide-body B747 aircraft. The objectives of the plan are:
— integration of existing systems;
— matching systems with available technology;
— using resources effectively;
— return on investment and time scale suitable for company needs.

Maintenance computer system
The elements of the maintenance computer system are:

Aircraft maintenance
This is known as OMEGA, which includes aircraft check planning, aircraft-maintenance check analysis and post-check analysis. Standard work packages are derived for the various checks, job cards for individual tasks are printed and distributed. Developments are the inclusion of unscheduled work tasks revealed by pre-check inspection, which account for around 50 per cent of the total workload on most checks, links with the TIME system for materials requisition, computer scheduling of jobs in a particular check and improvements in work documentation. The aim is to reduce aircraft time spent in the maintenance hangars and thus to improve availability for revenue service. The post-check analysis monitors results and helps engineers to find improvements.

Workshop production control
This includes workshop planning, component maintenance and ordering. It is closely linked to the TIME system, and the aim is to provide a tool for controlling and scheduling workshop production in order to match aircraft and component requirements. The ordering element will perform monitoring.

Total inventory management for engineering (TIME)
This incorporates materials management, inventory recording and stock audit. Inventory recording was the first phase of this project, now completed. Developments are now in the materials-management phase, using material requirement planning. In further developments, the stock audit will enable continuous monitoring of inventory position against targets, to guide future planning.

Costing
Cost control requires accurate recording of actual expenses, and forecasting for budgetary purposes.

Airworthiness
This ensures that all mandatory work required on an aircraft is correctly called up and actioned. It replaces various computer and paper based systems, which often replicated the same information. A single computer system will improve accuracy and response, to ensure safe operation of aircraft.

Automated time recording
This is part of the aircraft-maintenance and component-maintenance functions. The aim is to ensure that all work is properly planned and completed with minimum time wasted awaiting materials, tools, or further jobs. In future, subject to CAA approval, it is intended to have on-line certification of maintenance work.

Planning and control
Engineering activities are planned on many different time scales, areas of responsibility, and levels of detail. In separate offices these are difficult to coordinate. The master planning project aims to provide a single visible plan extending into all areas of the engineering organisation and covering all required time scales.

Operating aircraft control
This system is concerned with packaging fleet maintenance aircraft tasks, including routine work and allowable deferred defect (ADD) clearance, which are to be done

during a given aircraft turnround, and the allocation of appropriate staff and materials to ensure that each work package is completed on time.

OMEGA

OMEGA is the British Airways aircraft-maintenance production planning and control system, which is mainly concerned with base maintenance. It uses information technology to automate data collection and analysis needed for decisions made by supervisors and managers. Examples are:

— Visual display of job requirements, such as labour, materials, tools, equipment.
— Identification of all jobs needed to complete a particular aircraft check, or jobs requiring completion before a particular event during a check.
— Alerts to production engineers that ensure all time-controlled jobs are planned within their limits.

OMEGA relies on a database of over 27,000 jobs and 41,000 job cards, comprising all base maintenance planned at Heathrow airport and extending to planned maintenance at Gatwick Airport and then at Glasgow (regional aircraft). This involves transfer of the ex-BCAL data for Gatwick aircraft to the BA system with least disturbance. Developments of the system in hand are:

Inclusion of maintenance manual text with job cards. This requires redesign of the job card to permit relevant maintenance-manual extracts to be included with the job card, saving time of the maintenance worker. Provision of maintenance manuals in computer-readable form suitable for selective retrieval and printing has to be arranged from the aircraft manufacturers.

Unscheduled work capture. Details of all defects found during inspection and the rectification action taken are to be recorded by the system, together with the information necessary to control the job. This enables better production control and analysis, since all work on the aircraft is then contained in one system.

Job-time recording and control. Entry of actual job times to the system provides supervisors with better control of their task, eliminating the need to walk around looking at job cards in the rack. Analysis and display in various ways designed to make for easier understanding of the work progress in relation to the whole plan is possible with an interactive computer display.

Automatic demand of preselect items. Links to the TIME project enable materials needed for the work package to be requested from workshops at the right time and place.

Capacity planning. Comparison of available resources, such as labour, hangar bays, and special servicing equipment, with requirements of planned inputs will enable improved utilisation of these facilities. Recording of the actual use by each input will allow monitoring of plans.

Visit-number and planned-maintenance information. This is the use of an identity for each aircraft visit to base, so that labour and material cost comparisons can be made in sufficient detail.

Work scheduling. Initially this uses simple rules for sorting jobs within reporting codes or work areas. Further development is the construction of shift loading plans prior to the start of an aircraft input, based on assumed levels of unscheduled work. Later, the supervisor will be able to update the loading plan, so that the system can show the actual outstanding workload including unscheduled tasks and effects of actual resource availability.

On-line certification. This will accomplish the legal requirements of airworthiness regulations by computer validation instead of paper forms and signatures. Automatic updating of the technical records for aircraft will then be possible.

ENGINEERING ADP ON RAF OPERATIONAL STATIONS

Background

Recording of aircraft maintenance work in the Royal Air Force has always been necessary, and has increased with the growing complexity of aircraft. Records need to be kept of work done on the aircraft, its engines, and many other components. The requirement to track component lives, fatigue consumption, modification work, and special checks has increased the volume of detail. The information obtained by these actions is potentially useful, but extracting it and analysing the results from paper-based maintenance recording systems is often too lengthy to be justified except for serious problems. For these reasons, aircraft maintenance organisations have turned to computer-based recording systems as a solution to the difficulties of using information effectively.

The RAF maintenance data system

Recognising the need for data processing, the RAF set up the Maintenance Data Centre (MDC) at RAF Swanton Morley in 1969. The Unit's task was to collect, store in a computer, and analyse, maintenance information for the RAF and Fleet Air Arm (FAA). The Maintenance Data System (MDS) was first run on batch processing computers, using data from the standard MoD Form 720 (F720) job cards. A MOD study of future engineering information-technology requirements in the RAF led to the formation of the Maintenance Analysis and Computing Establishment (MACE) in 1984. As a result, the MDS computer was replaced by a more powerful system capable of on-line access. This enabled a change from routine report production to interactive analysis of the database on request from users. The first version relied on specialist staff (at MACE) to perform data interrogation and analysis for customers. It is anticipated that a system suitable for end-users at stations to interrogate will eventually be developed.

In addition to the upgrade to the MDS, MACE was also tasked with wider responsibilities including:

— Acquisition, analysis and dissemination of MDS data.
— Development, implementation and maintenance of engineering information-technology projects for the RAF, such as MDS and the Station Engineering Management Aid (SEMA).
— Development and support of small engineering-management computer systems.
— Management and development of MoD Form 700 series documentation to record all work performed on aircraft and their components.

In 1990 MACE was merged with the Supply Control Centre at RAF Stanbridge to form the RAF Logistics Establishment so that MACE has now become the Maintenance Analysis and Computing Division (MACD).

Reporting systems. The main sources of data are the F707B and F720 (Maintenance Work Order) documents which record faults and work on the aircraft and their equipment. These are used at all lines of maintenance, with appropriate differences in treatment. Older aircraft types for which full fault data is no longer needed have a reduced reporting policy.

Fatigue monitoring. Fatigue analysis for some aircraft is also performed at MACD. This is derived from a special record form, F725.

MACD Outputs. Emphasis has been placed on developing graphical presentation of results. Trends by any measure of age (airframe hours, calendar time, landings, starts, etc.) can be shown. Regular summaries in the style of management reports are circulated to user units and engineering authorities, and special enquiries are also dealt with.

Extension to RAF stations

The central database is useful to planning staff, aircraft fleet managers, and industry. It is less useful to first line operating units seeking information about technical problems. The data entry from paperwork is also inconvenient. Investigation of direct entry at stations was therefore begun, to assess the use of computer systems for the engineering function. This was found to be successful for routine data such as manhours, component changes, fatigue lives, and so on. The computer system was also found to be useful in checking the identity of components, by part number and description, against alternatives, thus saving demands being made outside the unit. Other benefits were:

— manpower reductions due to fewer staff being needed for recording;
— reduction of serviceable components sent outside;
— more accurate calculation of component lives.

This experience led to the specification of SEMA.

SEMA

SEMA was developed at the same time as another information system, the Station Administrative Management Aid (SAMA). These were integrated on the same hardware and also shared some software. The aim is to install it at Tornado and Phantom units. The main functions of SEMA are:

— aircraft records (engineering authorisations);
— personnel management;
— priority spares demand progression;
— catalogue.

Considering these further:

Aircraft records comprises component lifing, sortie information, scheduled maintenance, modifications, technical instructions and general statistics.

Component lifing may be in fatigue index, landings, airframe hours, or any other measure. A Component Life Register (CLR) is updated automatically for each component in use; changes on aircraft are also logged. This removes the need for much paper recording. Aircraft engines are treated similarly, so that life-critical parts are known.

Sortie information is input directly if possible, so that fatigue life and fatigue index may be updated.

Aircraft and component maintenance at all levels is recorded; forecasts of servicing due can be made easily.

Modifications, special technical instructions (STIs), servicing instructions (SIs), and any other mandatory tasks are recorded so that progress can be monitored.

Statistics are produced or extracted from the system to help users plan and control maintenance work. Users can obtain their own statistics.

Engineering personnel records can be examined by managers to check on qualifications for work and renewals needed.

Priority demands for urgent spares are simplified in the system by informing all users of the latest state. Thus shortages, the reason for demand, and the response are displayed to all those involved in the progress.

Catalogue of all parts shows application and interchangeability, and can be added to by local units.

Other systems

SEMA is not the only engineering-management system in the RAF, though it is one of the largest. Smaller systems exist to solve specific problems more quickly, using the same hardware and network. Examples are:

STAMA. This is the station transport ADP management aid, for use by MT sections. It is derived from a commercial vehicle fleet management system. This enabled faster introduction than by incorporating it in SEMA.

Microcomputers. Self-contained solutions based on microcomputers are developed by MACE for units with special requirements or without access to SEMA, such as non-flying stations. Connection of microcomputers to SEMA also provides local computing power to users of the main database without the inconvenience of data transfer by hand.

System integration

Computer systems are thus appearing in several ways at RAF stations, mostly under the supervision or control of MACD. Although systems were justified in their own right, their integration into a combined system would be still better. Data requirements could be shared, hardware could be standardised and management could control a wider range of functions. One other need is to reduce the proliferation of computer skills and training needed to operate the systems, since this limits growth.

The RAF, being a public sector customer, has tended to buy equipment of the same standard as other such users. Future standards, promoted as the Open Systems Interconnection (OSI) model, are being studied. Meanwhile, a decision to install station-wide Local Area Networks is being implemented. Connection to other RAF computer systems and to MoD systems is envisaged.

RAF-STRATEGY FOR THE FUTURE

The RAF aerosystems maintenance task

The aim of the RAF aerosystems maintenance organisation is to support the operational task by providing the engineering support which requires special facilities and skills. This task, which is carried out mainly within RAF Support Command, involves the repair and overhaul of most fixed-wing aircraft and their associated equipment for all three Services. This means doing the more complex maintenance work that is beyond the capability of the operational stations, or work which is cheaper to centralise.

Until its closure in July 1992, RAF Abingdon, together with RAF St Athan, carried out most of the aircraft maintenance work which is now, wholly, the responsibility of St Athan, where major servicing, modification and storage of Jaguar and Hawk aircraft is carried out.

St Athan is also the base of the Repair and Salvage Squadron which has world-wide responsibility for recovery of accident damaged aircraft for MoD and DoT. Battle damage repair schemes for aircraft and systems are also prepared there and specialist repair and maintenance teams are sent to units in the field when it is not convenient or feasible to return the damaged machine for repair.

As the largest engineering base, St Athan has both Service and civilian staff, and the widest range of tasks of the specialist repair units. Many aircraft types are handled, including Tornado, Phantom, and Harrier. It is the main centre for Tornado deep maintenance, planned to make more than 50 of these aircraft per year in the 1990s. St Athan also does engine repair and overhaul for about half the Adour engines of the Jaguar and Hawk, and the RB199 engine in the Tornado. St Athan is also the centre for the repair of mechanical and structural components on all aircraft types. Major repair and overhaul require spare parts, obtainable from industry is possible but often made locally to save cost and time. This has led to a design and manufacturing facility capable of solving unusual problems quickly and effectively.

Avionic equipment is repaired at RAF Sealand, again using Service and civilian staff at the same base. This centre repairs all kinds of avionic equipment for the three

Services which cannot be maintained at other units. Again, this includes Tornado items, but equipment of much older design is handled because manufacturer support is no longer available.

The job of the aerosystems maintenance organisation is to provide the best service at the right cost. The centres are accountable through the Executive Responsibility Budget system, which encourages them to make local decisions for contracting work.

Information technology objectives

Labour and equipment costs are the largest items of an engineering unit. Defence budgeting fixes cash limits on expenditure, which in turn place constraints on manpower and equipment levels. The utilisation of these must therefore be maximised. The Executive Responsibility Budget (ERB) makes local management accountable for costs and is required to achieve stated tasks within an agreed budget. Staff costs are the largest single budget item, therefore accurate labour recording is essential for good management. Maintenance tasks specify turnround times, on which other operational plans depend, so adherence to these times is important.

The information technology (IT) objectives are therefore to provide the means to achieve these aims. Computer systems need to be suitable for engineering work, including a presence in workshops or hangars. Savings in the cost and time of maintenance work are required to justify the expenditure on computer systems.

The maintenance IT strategy

The systems used must, for example, be capable of labour recording, inventory control and progress, work planning, statistical analysis, technical records, and possibly forecasting and simulation of work. The approach is first to develop on-line methods of manpower recording and work movement, using standard industrial data capture techniques. This provides the basic accurate data needed for further requirements, which include management reporting and control systems. The later stages involve linking to other Service data systems. Access to all this data has to be obtained as easily and quickly as possible, a requirement which makes user interface design and standards important. The kind of activity expected on the computer is direct examination of stock levels, priority progress of urgent spares, use of parts catalogues, and eventually ordering through other computer systems.

Where possible, proven commercial software is used, such as critical path analysis packages, production-inventory systems and management information systems. In some cases a locally produced system is devised.

IT development plan

Computer systems for maintenance were first developed for local use, and were not conceived as part of an overall strategy. They were of limited use for control and information purposes, being run on batch-processing machines. The current strategy for aerosystems maintenance in RAF Support Command has an investment of £20M over 10 years; the estimated savings in this period exceed £40M, through clerical-staff reductions, lower stock holdings, and other productivity increases.

A system based on ICL computers has been selected, using 4th generation application generators to provide the specified software. Other features needed for data collection and processing, local computing, and specialist tasks can be added. A major objective is to define common database standards for everyone to work from. Maintenance Units have been given the task of developing their particular system to fit into the strategy. Thus RAF Sealand develops the management reporting system used in executive responsibility budgets, RAF Abingdon developed the PERT system used in aircraft major maintenance, whilst RAF St Athan develops the mechanical-component maintenance system and its interface to the MDS at CSDE.

The future

In 1988, a strategic study of the RAF's overall longer-term logistics IT requirements was commissioned. The resultant 10 year plan, known as the Logistics IT Strategy (LITS), is now in the final stages of gaining approval and funding. Its aim is to provide an integrated and coherent set of logistics IT functionality for the entire RAF's logistics community by the turn of the century. Hence, the shortcomings identified earlier in this chapter have been addressed by the LITS and should be resolved with its introduction.

ARTIFICIAL INTELLIGENCE

Introduction

Artificial intelligence (AI) is a type of computer software capable of using rules supplied by a programmer with information given by a user to produce inferences. The term originated in an attempt to distinguish it from previous procedural programs, but its relation to human intelligence is arguable, despite the popular press talk of robot brains. Computers can be programmed, after a great deal of research, to perform remarkable but specific tasks such as beating a grand master at chess. Making a computer assist in general problem-solving is some way off yet. In the present context, artificial intelligence should be thought of as an elaborate kind of database.

One goal of AI workers is natural language processing (NLP); in short, a computer that understands ordinary human speech, or accepts plain English descriptions for search conditions in a database. As the use of computers widens to people who are not computer specialists, this becomes more important. Vision systems are also being studied as AI applications, and are used in industrial robotics. Computer systems that use rules and knowledge to solve problems are referred to as 'expert systems'. They are useful in engineering as an aid to solving intricate problems which cannot be reduced to simple equations. One class of these problems is planning; AI-based scheduling programs are on trial in a number of industries, as an aid to the planner rather than as a complete replacement for the human. Other uses of expert systems are expected to be in training aids and for fault-finding or diagnostic purposes.

In many ways, AI has yet to live up to the promises first made for it. The actual extent of industrial robots, in the sense of machines that require little programming, is only a small part of the entire machine tool market. Software for AI is still largely in the experimental stage, and subject to frequent revisions. This makes some users reluctant to get involved with it.

Expert systems

Expert systems are a way of storing special human talents for use by others. Without this, companies relying on the acquired skills of their employees, often built up over time in the absence of formal training, are vulnerable to the loss or retirement of these specialists. A method of preserving continuity and saving the expense of re-training is attractive. It may be expected that some of the human experts will object to the idea of their work being reduced to a set of rules and put away forever, but the complete replacement of humans by machines in this area still seems remote.

Expert systems are made with rules; rules need logic to be described. The process of reducing human expertise to an adequate set of rules is usually lengthy for any application regarded as being worth the building of an expert system. Like good engineering, this ought to be regarded as a trade-off between performance and cost, but making the developers of such systems accept this can be a test of management. Most projects in which the managers assume that it will be safe to leave specification to the computer staff end by pleasing the computer people, not the managers.

Expert systems can be classed as rule-based, model-based, or knowledge-based. Rule-based expert systems are, as the title implies, collections of rules without any further insight. Thus one rule may say that a certain result is associated with a particular condition, without explaining why this happens. Many medical systems are like this, reflecting an imperfect understanding of physiology, so it may be expected that engineering systems of this kind will be useful.

Model-based expert systems augment the empirical rules with some knowledge. This would be a good method when quantitative data is used with a mathematical model of the system, such as avionics or gas-turbine thermodynamics, but not for structural corrosion.

Knowledge-based expert systems have, in effect, rules about the rules to be used in given situations. This is sometimes called meta-knowledge and is one of the most active research areas.

Selecting problems for expert systems is a skill. They should be sufficiently complicated to justify the effort, but not so difficult that development of a system within reasonable time and computer storage is impossible. Thus it is unlikely that an expert system capable of planning the fleet schedule for a large airline is feasible, but parts of the problem, such as allocation of resources to aircraft turnrounds, may be soluble. Planning in a small airline is simpler, but asking a government regulatory body to decide how many small airlines are better than one big one is another complicated question.

Before computers, production control in aircraft maintenance was done in the heads of progress chasers. The introduction of computers to inventory and production control allowed simple rules to be applied to large amounts of data, taking away much of the old skills required. Seat reservation in airlines has long been a subject for computers; analysts had just about got a system working on the few seat classes in the era of all-scheduled flights when a new array of non-scheduled tickets arrived and altered this. Now some yield-management systems seem to work by dividing the airline activity into areas for a human manager to administer.

Expert systems in aircraft maintenance training

The object of this project was not just to use an expert system for fault diagnosis, but also to improve operators' understanding of the equipment's function and thus to make them better maintenance technicians. Most managers accept that maintenance technicians with a good understanding of how the equipment works are superior at fault diagnosis to those with less knowledge, and this is the basis of traditional maintenance training, which consists of detailed explanations of system function in a classroom, backed up by study of the actual hardware.

The growing complexity of aircraft equipment, with the lower frequency of some faults as reliability increases, has made this type of training and experience harder to develop. Shortage of skilled staff also aggravates this problem, and has led to an interest in alternative methods. Research has shown that good troubleshooting technicians use a mental approach which enables them to diagnose problems which they have not previously met. This is based on a 'mental model' of the system operation. An artificial aid should therefore be possible, and would act as a useful training aid and job performance indicator. In a case of extreme urgency, the expert system could be used straight away; with more time available it would act as a tuition method.

Simulation

The method uses qualitative simulation; this models qualitative causal reasoning. Variables are assigned a few values, such as zero, low, high, rather than all possibilities. This is adequate for maintenance instruction. The model consists of interconnected elements each of which is a set of rules defining the apparent operation of the system. It is not necessary to know precisely how failure modes affect performance, so the number of states is restricted to essentials such as on/off, normal/failed, and so on.

Jet engine diagnostic

This system comprises the simulation program, the expert system diagnostic, the knowledge base, and the user interface. Software is written in a suitable high-level language. The system is represented as a set of components (pump, filter, actuator, etc.) which interact in specific ways corresponding to their real behaviour.

The knowledge base has rules and facts about the components. These are similar to the descriptions given by instructors to a class learning from a conventional schematic diagram, but expressed in the program language.

The simulation model consists of the components needed, e.g. for an oil system there are fewer than ten items, a simplified version of the actual. A graphical interface shows a schematic diagram with controls and instrument displays imitating the real versions. Controls are activated by a pointing device such as a mouse or a touchpad.

In use, the learner can operate the controls and watch the response. Faults can then be deliberately introduced for certain components in order to study their effects. A typical sequence would be to select a faulty component and then pretend to start the engine. If the simulation model adequately represents the essential features and performance of the real engine, then symptoms will be shown in the sequence and form similar to those that would be produced in a real engine. This is especially helpful when faults are transient. If the user wishes to confirm a diagnosis, then the state of any component can be checked by 'inspecting' it using a secondary menu on the computer screen. A session can be recorded and played back for confirmation.

Alternatively, the student can select the expert system for diagnosis, which proceeds through a sequence of question and answer steps until the fault is isolated.

Expert system building

The system requires definition of the faults expected; this has to be a selection of all those possible in a real system. The relevant symptoms are then defined in a similar way. A fault isolation tree is then drawn, the root being the primary symptom, such as no oil pressure indicated, and the remainder being other symptoms, in order of time taken to verify. A tree may have hundreds of branches when finished. For the original computer model, a limited number of rules were chosen and a common sub-system only was represented, to keep construction work and time down. The program ran on a workstation which would now cost under $10,000. Development took ten man-days, including testing. The result was still only a prototype, constructed to demonstrate the use of qualitative models. One conclusion drawn from the exercise was the need to simplify the problem being studied, and the length of the knowledge-engineering phase which defines the problem and derives the rules. Programming was less difficult.

Further development

Recommendations were that more explanation be added to the job performance function in the system, possibly from a videodisc system showing more realistic pictures, another that an intelligent tutor be provided, using an expert system as an instructor instead of as a diagnostic.

Expert system for gas turbine engine diagnosis

This was developed by Textron Lycoming Division to aid maintenance staff. A combination of instrument readings and operator replies uses knowledge gained from experienced technicians and design engineers to assist others in servicing a helicopter gas turbine engine.

The principles of maintenance can be stated in four steps:

— Establish the condition of the engine;
— Isolate any fault present, or failed part;
— Decide on the appropriate remedy and perform it;
— Confirm that the fault has been cured.

The condition-monitoring ingredient has four elements:

Engine performance measurement. This is necessary to establish whether the power is sufficient for the intended mission.

Trend forecasting. It should be possible to estimate when performance limits will be exceeded, given present values and rates of change over time.

Event monitoring. Single events which can affect engine life, such as overspeed, or overtemperature, need to be recorded automatically because reliance on constant human vigilance is unrealistic.

Life monitoring. Low cycle fatigue (LCF), creep and thermal fatigue affect the life of parts.

Diagnosis is made by analysing condition-monitoring data and noting crew or maintenance technician comments to find the defect. This may be a simple breakage, or an interaction between parts of the system. Repair or re-adjustment is done according to procedures described in the approved maintenance manuals.

The engine chosen for this project was not a new type, in fact it had been in use for nearly thirty years. The reason for this was the nature of faults experienced and the technology used. It used hydro-mechanical control and actuation, with few externally measurable parameters, so human observations were necessary for diagnosis. Many engines of this type remain in use, therefore improvement in serviceability would yield large benefits.

The expert system is knowledge-based, constructed by a knowledge engineer working with several technical sources. These include experienced maintenance technicians, design staff involved in theoretical analysis, measurements of actual engines available, details of past history for all engines of the type. The result is coded as a computer program with an easily used display requiring no special skill to operate it. In operation, the expert system analyses the data supplied, requests additional information if necessary, and then recommends action. Guidance for confirming clearance of the fault is also provided.

Project work began with a small-scale prototype model using standard software available for building expert systems. This was confined to engine starting and high exhaust-temperature faults, and ran on a portable computer. Much of the knowledge was taken from the manufacturer's manuals, enabling development in one man-week. Following this, a more structured project was started in conjunction with a research organisation. The project used software already well established in AI work, with nearly 200 rules. Some relations are described in probability terms, others in logic.

In operation the system is like the procedure used without an expert system. The technician first attempts to solve the problem alone; if this fails then a senior technical staff member is sought. If local staff cannot solve a problem, then company specialists or manufacturer's representatives are asked. An expert system embodies all these in one place, if it is updated frequently.

The full system runs on a workstation with a graphical display having the available options displayed, so the user only has to select one. Records may be kept of each session, for future reference or transmission to other users. An analysis of benefits showed returns equal to 12 times the cost for this system, stemming from shorter maintenance times, fewer unjustified removals, and better engine performance.

MAINTENANCE OF SOFTWARE

Introduction

Many modern aircraft systems use digital electronics for signalling and control. The instructions for these functions may be hard-wired as logic circuits, embedded in programmable devices, or stored in removable magnetic media for use in volatile memory when needed. This is 'software' even if the aircraft stores it in hardware for safety purposes, since the manufacturer may have written the instructions on a development system. Storage such as magnetic disk or tape is too delicate for safe use on aircraft, so read-only memories are used. Examples are navigation systems, radar signal processors, engine controls and flight management computers.

The operator who uses digital avionics may encounter defects in the component or system that result from hardware failures or from software faults. This means that development of the software needs to be managed, in addition to hardware maintenance as practised with non-digital equipment. It is not usual for operators to have authority to modify their own software, particularly in systems critical for flight safety. The operator is therefore dependent on the equipment supplier for diagnosis and correction of software faults.

Military experience

Military operators have longer experience of software management than civil users, since the earliest uses of airborne software were for functions required in military aircraft and ground systems. Examples were anti-submarine work and guided weapons. The RAF set up a specialist branch for operational software support in the 1960s, for both airborne and ground-based systems. The main objective was to achieve improvement in the speed and cost of software changes, and to have the degree of control necessary in war. Contractors could not always be expected to do this in the way required by the RAF. Another difficulty was that contractors tended to give priority in staffing to development of new software and systems, so reducing support for existing equipment. A further reason given for having internal software development teams was the insight gained into the working of systems and the ability to use this in the specification of future requirements.

Aircraft design is very conservative when the raw materials or essential components are considered, and digital technology is no exception to this. Nothing is used in an aircraft until it has been thoroughly proved and understood in laboratory and ground tests. This means that some airborne digital equipment appears rather simple by comparison with what is currently available elsewhere. Originally this necessitated the use of airborne computers with small memory capacity, and diagnostic output in the form of plain bit-patterns. However, progress has led to memories of megabyte sizes, user-programmable diagnostics, bus-linked modules, graphical displays intelligible to flight crew, and other refinements. Military users have 'smart' weapons, electronic countermeasures, data encryption, and other complications not met by civilian operators. Civilian communications and navigation are 'open systems' with substantial user bases to rely on. Civil equipment is generally sold in a more price-conscious market, and this may lead to performance restriction in the non-critical systems, so that the obvious remedy of upgrading to cure a fault may not be justifiable. Inflight entertainment systems suffer from this policy, unless the marketing department conveys a sense of urgency to the technical department.

RAF methods

The RAF method of implementing software support is intended to minimise the total costs of buying and using an avionic system. This is done, first, by incorporating formal standards and engineering measures in the specifications of requirements; second, by formulating a software support policy at the start of a project.

Support of in-service operational software is regarded as an engineering responsibility, just as for traditional hardware. This results in resources being provided according to the level of support decided upon. This may be:

Total Service support. A team is established at a Service unit, capable of all in-service support. The Service thus becomes the design authority for the software.

Total industry support. All design and production is the industry's responsibility. The Service performs acceptance testing, and retains the right to control release of the software.

Joint Service/industry support. This may be done by assigning teams made up of Service and contractor staff at Service establishments, by placing Service representatives with the contractor, or by defining at what level the work changes from a Service task to industry support.

Standard software is industry-supported. This may mean that source code written by the Service is their responsibility, but the development system that converts it to machine language, and the hardware processor, are contractor functions. This requires careful documentation to isolate these areas from possible confusion.

Software support policy

Co-ordination. Long lead times of defence systems make it necessary to consider software support early in a project.

System. The kind of project is important in deciding the software support. Features which may affect the extent of in-service modification and likelihood of external support are identified and used to influence the decision.

Skills. Expertise not available to the user, such as design of software critical to flight safety, rules out in-service support in these cases. The amount of pre-delivery testing and certification work is expected to result in software not requiring much alteration. RAF support teams conform to the same quality standards as those for contractors.

Design. After delivery of the system, design authorities retain an interest in the progress of certification, which often requires performance to be demonstrated in service. The operator's team has to co-ordinate this activity and the introduction of any revisions resulting from the process. The user may also initiate changes by request to the contractor; this can be difficult if the contractor has not been prepared for such an event. To overcome this, the RAF has instituted a policy of requiring their own software and staff to work to the same standards as those of the contractor.

Control. This consists of quality and change aspects. Quality control of military software is performed to NATO standards and audited regularly by independent specialists. Configuration changes to software are reviewed by boards of representatives as part of the aircraft project.

Software support progress

The support needs for early software systems were much simpler than for current systems. A single computer, a low-level (assembler) language and simple storage (PROM) may once have been sufficient; now teams using high-level (ADA or FORTRAN) languages on computer networks with large mass storage are needed. The growth in size and complexity of modern software demands management techniques capable of handling these features. Technical standards are an important part of this practice; this means a large volume of documentation and testing.

Tools. Well-known products with good support are preferred, proven by the experience of the user or of other customers. New methods are evaluated against this guideline. The existence of a military standard for avionic hardware support (MIL-STD-1388) has prompted the search for a software equivalent: Support Analysis for Software (SAS). This is to be used in the European Fighter Aircraft (EFA) project.

Staff. Large teams in software projects are now common. This raises some new problems in management of skills, and the familiar one of losses from the military to the civil field.

Emergencies. Analysts or programmers are not traditionally regarded as frontline service personnel; this may have to change if maintenance of the software is critical to operations in battle, or other operations away from base.

Other effects. Interdependence of software and hardware, and of some software between different projects, makes it important to ensure that interchangeability is achieved. Examples are the compatibility of software in simulators and in the actual aircraft.

Safety-critical systems

Software is now being used to provide control in systems essential to flight safety, such as stability augmentation. This has very high requirements for reliability, and assurance must be given that no danger will be introduced by relying on software. Among the methods under study for this are:

— analysis techniques, similar in principle to the failure-mode and effect analysis of hardware;
— exact specifications which can be verified independently;
— code-analysis tools available for high-level languages;
— special microprocessors with emphasis on integrity;
— proven development systems certified for aircraft use;
— management systems enabling close control and review.

Some of these have been developed for military use, others are available from the computer industry to meet similar needs in civil or non-aircraft projects. This is an area of active research by the industry, and significant progress is expected.

Conclusion

The RAF aim in software support is to improve quality and rate of progress while reducing the total life-cycle costs, and to impose requirements on suppliers which attain these objectives, especially in relation to safety-critical systems. As an operator, the RAF regards long-term support as vital.

CHAPTER 6 TECHNOLOGY IN AIRCRAFT MAINTENANCE

ONBOARD MAINTENANCE SYSTEMS

Onboard maintenance systems are the latest development in aircraft avionics. They began with simple 'press-to-test' buttons and failure flags fitted to individual items in the cockpit. These required human action and recorded no data. Autopilot systems were the driving force behind development of a better maintenance system to embrace all of the autopilot's functions and its components, with the intention of meeting the integrity and certification requirements of autoland. The very high safety level specified for autoland could only be attained using redundancy in a system; this implied self-test and reporting to establish that the system was functioning correctly. In the early analogue electronic autoland systems this remained part of the components, but the introduction of airborne digital computers made it possible to use a central computer for monitoring and display of system performance.

A dedicated maintenance control and display unit (MCDP) was fitted to Boeing 757 and 767 aircraft, which entered service in the early 1980s. The similar function on Boeing 737 aircraft was automated using the control and display unit (CDU) of the performance data computer (PDC) for the 737-200 series, and the flight management computer (FMC) of the 737-300 series aircraft.

The Boeing 757 and 767 also introduced the engine indicating and crew alerting system (EICAS) — part of the 'glass cockpit', as it is popularly known. This is a maintenance-significant system, with maintenance data displays for engines, APU, electrical, hydraulic, and environmental control systems. In addition, despatch-critical maintenance data are displayed in the form of status messages as part of the caution and warning function.

The Boeing 747-400 central maintenance computer (CMC) system evolved from the 757/767 EICAS and MCDP. The CMC connects to most aircraft systems which use electronics. One of its primary functions is to relate these system-fault signals with observable flight deck effects, such as EICAS caution, warning and status messages display flags, or other visual/aural indications.

Ingredients of an onboard maintenance system

Boeing considers the following features to be essential elements of an onboard maintenance system:

1. A fault detection and reporting function in all member systems capable of:
— detecting and isolating all system internal faults to the line replaceable unit (LRU) level;
— detecting faults in the LRU input interfaces;

— testing the system and its interfaces for proper operation and functionality;
— storing internally the LRU fault data for later shop maintenance.

2. A central maintenance computer capable of:
— receiving and processing fault and situation data from member systems;
— correlating fault data to possible flight deck effects;
— consolidating fault data to isolate the root cause of cascading fault conditions;
— initiating tests to verify the integrity of all member systems;
— providing a common point for control and display of all maintenance functions using plain English formats;
— processing and formatting output data for printing, recording, or transfer to another place;
— providing a common point for distribution of time, flight phase, flight leg transitions, and similar events, for use by member systems;
— recording of airplane condition monitoring (ACM) data, including manually and automatically initiated events.

3. A documentation system describing the use of the onboard maintenance system.

Standards

Standards for maintainability of avionic equipment are produced by the US Airlines Electronic Engineering Committee (AEEC) as Aeronautical Radio Inc. (ARINC) publications, including:

ARINC 415 — Operation and test guidance for failure monitoring and functional test.
ARINC 604 — Guidance for design and use of built-in test equipment (BITE), 1985 (preceded by ARINC 423).
ARINC 612 — BITE glossary, 1986.
ARINC 624 — Onboard maintenance systems (supersedes all previous).

ARINC 624 covers all facets of an OMS, including member systems BITE, central maintenance computer fault-recording and display, aircraft condition monitoring, electronic storage and retrieval of maintenance data. The contractor responsible for system integration, usually the aircraft manufacturer, has to rely on these standards, especially when offering options to the airline customer. Airlines with fleets from different aircraft manufacturers will then be able to benefit from standardisation of maintenance systems. It was a complaint of aircraft buyers in the early stages of test equipment that every manufacturer seemed to recommend a different set of test gear, and that operators found it difficult to obtain advance technical specifications in sufficient detail to enable standard test programs to be written.

Reliability and maintainability of digital avionics

Digital systems have proved to be reliable because of their self-test ability. However, this also causes problems in workshops when reported faults cannot be confirmed on test. Operators have learnt that some faults are transient, and are not repeatable. Reasons for this can be:

differences between predicted and real environment
airline maintenance practices
equipment design problems

Results of one survey (Boeing 737-300 FMCS) are shown in Table 6.1.
Data of this nature is expected to be provided by customer airlines, but not all of them do this completely. Avionics suppliers can obtain the data when they also repair

Table 6.1 Results of one survey (Boeing 737-300 FMCS)

Category	Number	%
Failure confirmed by shop test	177	46
Failure confirmed by BITE	123	32
Software design problem	35	9
Insufficient data	26	7
Wrong LRU rejected	23	6
Total	384	100
Flight hours	914,000	

the units, but they may be unwilling to publish it. A Boeing comment is that suppliers generally seem to ignore what their own BITE tells them.

Reliability is measured by mean time between failures (MTBF). Manufacturers count failures as those confirmed by shop test. This leads to the usual disagreement between operators and suppliers over the unconfirmed removal rate, with the implication that it is due to maintenance errors from the operator.

A better solution is to count all internal failures detected by the more accurate BITE system. The data in Table 6.1 has 177 (46 per cent) removals confirmed by shop test, but a failure confirmed by BITE in 123 more (32 per cent) cases. Thus MTBF is only a measure of hard faults and not an indication of the usability of the equipment. The traditional manufacturer's response might be something like 'half of them are not wrong on test, so they are not our problem', whereas the operator's response to this might have been 'half of them are removed because we cannot find out what is wrong with them on the aircraft'. Other lines of argument from the operator centre on the observation that, although the unit might pass a shop test, its replacement demonstrably cleared an aircraft system fault — with the implication that the shop test is not adequate.

Mean time between unscheduled removals (MTBUR) is a better measure of total performance. It is affected by maintenance skills, but it also lets out the cases where transient faults are cleared by switching off and on again, to the manufacturer's benefit. MTBUR is easily measured from operator's records, but only the operator may know what it is, since suppliers only receive the rejected units.

What is needed is a failure-rate measuring system which includes confirmation by the BITE and recognition of design errors. This would force designers to rely on BITE and improve its integrity. Faults indicated by BITE would have to be corrected; if BITE itself is wrong, then improve the BITE accuracy.

Hard and soft failures

Digital avionics specialists distinguish 'hard', 'soft', and 'intermittent' failures. A hard failure is one that persists through several attempts to start the system. A soft failure is one where failure symptoms disappear when power is recycled or when a BITE test is run. An intermittent fault is one which disappears without any obvious operator action.

Soft failures are the greatest area of concern for digital avionics; they may be a combination of hardware faults and software errors. Intermittent faults are more of a nuisance than a danger, but can consume too much maintenance time in attempts to locate them. BITE records can be useful in these problems; if an intermittent fault keeps recurring, then a deeper investigation may be worthwhile. These intermittent and soft failures in avionics are the source of erratic maintenance practices, sometimes called 'shotgun maintenance'. A common practice when maintenance staff are unsure of the cause of a fault involving avionics is to work through the system; thus the transducer is first changed, then the amplifier/processor, then the indicator, and so on until the fault disappears.

BITE is a common term in the industry, used to mean that part of the system which performs the maintenance function. In most digital avionics the equipment part of built-in test equipment includes some hardware and much software.

BIT, for built-in test, means something completely different from BITE, a source of confusion. BIT is generally used to refer to the fault and error detection functions of a system whose primary purpose is to protect the pilot and the aircraft from bad or misleading displays or commands. This fault detection function is therefore part of the basic operational function of the system.

For software certification purposes this is an important distinction. The maintenance function, or BITE, is classed as non-essential for safety. The fault detection function, or BIT, is a basic part of a system classed as essential or critical and must be certified to the same standard as that system.

BITE and BIT confusion increases when discussing BITE integrity, because this is usually taken as the ability of BITE to reliably detect and report faults and/or failures, but the primary fault detection monitors are part of the basic system function. BITE may use the results of these inbuilt operational monitors, but the monitors themselves are not part of BITE. Exceptions would be monitors or tests which act at power on or at operator request. ARINC 624 resolves this by omitting reference to BIT and defining BITE to be the total maintenance function of a system.

Airline maintenance practice

The assumption in maintenance procedures defined in manufacturers' manuals for avionic equipment is that the operator's line servicing staff will only perform maintenance in response to a crew report of a problem, entered in a technical log. The flight crew may see signs of a system fault, such as a caution or warning, a system disconnect, or a discrepancy between readings. This is referred to, as in US terminology, as a flight deck effect (FDE). The relation of system faults and flight deck effects is a key feature of the aircraft maintenance system design.

US manufacturers' practice on recent designs has been to have:

— a fault reporting manual (FRM), which defines numerical fault codes for flight crew reporting of flight deck effects;
— a fault isolation manual (FIM), which defines the maintenance action required for each FRM code.

The two systems together are sometimes referred to as FIRM, for fault isolation and reporting method. It is very bureaucratic in use, and one survey of the extent to which several major airlines used it in practice showed that only in one country could the use be said to be complete.

On the latest aircraft, such as Boeing 747-400, the fault isolation manual also identifies the central maintenance computer fault code which could be related to each FRM code. This works well with aircraft having a central caution and warning system like EICAS.

Older aircraft, such as Boeing 737-300, which do not have EICAS, do not use FIRM. Their maintenance manuals rely on the line maintenance staff being able to identify the ATA chapter of the system fault described in the crew report, and then use a troubleshooting guide to locate the faulty system.

Prior to the introduction of CMC systems, a pilot report on one aircraft system led to the BITE for that system being interrogated, but other systems did not always have their BITE readings taken, so unreported failures could go unchecked. With a CMC system indicating all faults on one display, it is harder to ignore failures recorded with no corresponding flight crew report.

Use of BITE for in-service performance tracking

The BITE fault stored inside an LRU is often the only useful data to assist in failure investigation. It is therefore important that shop staff record and track BITE records of all LRUs received. BITE data must be credible if maintenance work is to be based on it.

Correlating repair records with users' complaints is laborious, especially if log entries give no more than the too common cryptic 'U/S', 'failed', or less complimentary terms. Complex software faults need a full description of events to be reproducible in a shop test. Manual data will probably never be adequate for this. An integrated maintenance system can perform much better.

Avionics suppliers must keep records of equipment repairs and BITE data. Memory for BITE data recording is now cheap and big enough to record much useful data,

Plate 16 Avionics test systems

such as phase of flight, aircraft and route, location of fault, state of the system at that time, and so on. The event recording frequency of modern BITE systems is programmable by users, a useful feature if learnt.

Aircraft manufacturers have complained about apparent lack of consultation between equipment designers and servicing organisations. Designers should try to provide a system which performs throughout its life, and therefore be aware of in-service performance by their equipment. Too often the complaint is that designers move on to the next generation of equipment and abandon thinking about improving the present generation. Feedback of service behaviour should be a high priority, leading to better reliability and maintainability. One approach to this problem is to lengthen the phase in which the designer/manufacturer is contractually responsible for equipment, from one-year 'warranty periods' to several years.

ENGINE MONITORING

Introduction

Engine monitoring embraces several techniques, oil analysis, gas path analysis, usage measurement. The analytical approach is usually referred to as 'engine health monitoring', and is the preferred method of condition monitoring for aircraft engines. This attempts to measure whether the engine is operating within acceptable performance limits, and also if any trend in the performance values indicates a need for intervention. The objective is to anticipate maintenance events and plan them at convenient opportunities, instead of being forced to take action in circumstances that would disrupt planned flying schedules.

Oil analysis includes filter contents checks, microscopic visual examination of particles recovered from filters, metallographic and spectrographic analysis of oil samples in laboratories.

Gas path analysis takes the readings of engine thermodynamic parameters such as temperature, pressure, fuel flow, shaft speed, and reduces them to standard day values for comparison with the manufacturer's performance specification for the engine type.

Plate 17 Turbine blade inspection techniques

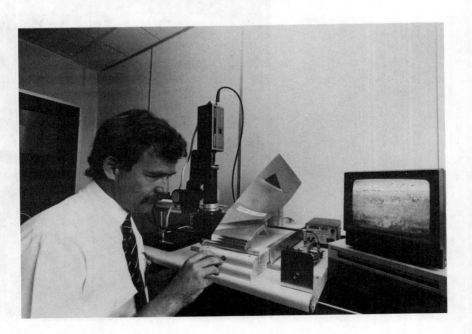

Engine Monitoring

Originally the data was noted by flight deck crew from cockpit gauges and then copied from the technical log form for computer input. Later, airborne transducers and recorders were used to acquire data automatically, this being an additional function of mandatory flight data accident recorders in the UK; results and action still had to be processed after the flight at a remote site. More recently, the possibility of transmitting data directly from the aircraft to the ground, or of analysing data for diagnosis in flight, has arrived with recent developments in telecommunications and computers.

Usage measurement was traditionally done by cycle counting, assuming an average duty cycle for the engine part from take-off to touchdown. This procedure is necessary for the more temperature-critical and fatigue-limited parts of the engine, such as discs and turbine blades. With newer advanced methods of airborne measurement and analysis, it is possible to obtain a more accurate estimate of the cumulative use of life for these parts, and so use them more effectively.

Trend analysis system

A typical example of the modern approach to turbine engine monitoring is the system developed jointly by the engine and airframe manufacturers with three European airlines operating the General Electric CF6 engines on Airbus aircraft, and later extended to the CF6 engines on the Boeing 747 and McDonnell Douglas DC10 aircraft. The primary objective was to achieve high on-time service to passengers and to control operating costs by minimising engine unscheduled maintenance, particularly away from the airline's home base when operations are worldwide.

Parameters

The computer system is able to monitor and analyse many engine thermodynamic and mechanical measurements in one program. These include engine performance in cruise, in take-off and on test bed, vibration readings, engine control settings, and performance simulation. Monitoring ability includes extraction of routine data, and also automatic trend recognition and alert warning. Data stored in the computer can be analysed by users for their own needs. Software development by the engine manufacturer for the basic analysis and performance tasks required by all operators reduces support costs of the system. The airlines are able to concentrate on implementation and use of the system, giving feedback to the manufacturers about useful features.

Each airline is responsible for acquiring its own data and supplying it to the program in an agreed format. This may be done by a quick-change tape cassette connected to the aircraft flight data recorder (FDR). This separates the non-essential function of engine monitoring from the mandatory requirements of the FDR, so the engine-data cassette does not have to be protected against accident damage and is therefore easily accessible by ground staff. The tape cassette is then forwarded to an analysis section for copying onto larger media. More recent developments in this area use direct connection to the airline central computer system by an interface located at the airport terminal gate — the ground engineer has only to plug in a cable for a few minutes. In future such data can be signalled airborne by the aircraft communication and reporting system (ACARS).

Engine parameters recorded and analysed include engine shaft speeds, exhaust gas temperature, engine pressure ratio, vibration levels, fan rotor imbalance, oil temperature, pressure and contents, fuel flow rate, control settings, bleed valve or inlet guide vane settings, significant events. Aircraft performance parameters needed for correlation and data reduction include ambient temperature and pressure, velocity and Mach number, altitude, phase of flight, time, control lever position.

Data processing and output is done automatically by the main computer program, showing trends of the main thermodynamic and mechanical variables with warning signs if detected. It is usual to use graphical plots, since large amounts of quantitative data are easier to examine in this way than tables of figures. Early analysis programs presented data for all engines, regardless of significance, and left it to the engine analyst to discover trends using his knowledge and experience of the type. This was tedious, therefore methods of screening results before display have been developed. The use of interactive terminals instead of routine printouts also helps to reduce wasted effort.

Examination of these trends is capable of detecting certain faults, such as compressor or turbine deterioration affecting efficiency, and increased vibration possibly caused by uneven blade wear or damage. The existence of such a monitoring system also assures airworthiness authorities that an on-condition engine maintenance program with minimum use of hard time lives will not compromise safety.

The ideal defect for this analysis is one that develops slowly and persistently, because the analysis may occur a day or two after the event and must be used to determine the cause and recommend action to line or base maintenance staff. Other useful tasks performed by some airlines include onboard calibration of engine control settings, without the need to perform ground engine runs. Apart from the cost saving, this satisfies the increasing desire of airport authorities to ban engine ground runs in the interest of better community relations.

Defects that are not so amenable to this analysis are those which may develop very quickly, such as certain kinds of ingestion damage, those which do not manifest themselves as instrument readings, and those where deviation is within the margin of error for the instrumentation used. One airline reported inconclusive results in attempting to use trend analysis for detecting excess aircraft drag by measuring fuel consumption. When an aircraft was isolated as suspect and taken off service for investigation, nothing unusual could be found by visual examination and dimensional checks of it.

Another problem with this kind of system is that it depends on the accuracy of sensors fitted to the aircraft, often as part of the normal flight instrument system. Should a fault develop in that system resulting in a transducer change, the trend program may have to recalibrate itself, leaving it 'blind' for a few flights.

Alert reporting

The CF6 engine monitoring system has incorporated alert reporting to give the user indications of abnormal situations which require corrective maintenance action. These alerts can apply either to a single parameter, as measured during engine operation, or to a parameter which is computed from the input data. The alerts as initially defined were:

— exhaust gas temperature (EGT), measured between the high pressure turbine (HPT) and low pressure turbine (LPT);
— vibration of the low pressure and the high pressure spools in twin-spool turbofans;
— EGT margin, a projection of the difference between the certified maximum allowable value and that predicted to occur during a full-rated take-off at sea level and hot-day limit conditions;
— EGT margin trend shift, a plot of the EGT margin against flight cycles; sudden shifts in this can indicate a possible engine problem.

Some of these derived parameters are useful because it is modern operating practice to use engine derating in service where possible. This takes advantage of the fact that airport runways are often longer than needed for full-power take-off, and the aircraft itself is not flying at full load or maximum ambient temperature, which require high thrust settings. The consequence is a useful reduction in stress-related engine costs, but deterioration of full-power thrust may go unnoticed if it is rarely used.

These alerts are intended for use by engineering and maintenance staff, and do not replace the cockpit gauge indications used by flight deck crew. Ideally, the E&M staff should be able to act before a flight deck effect appears.

Trend reporting

The format of standard reports made available to users is:

— take-off engine performance EGT deviation and LP/HP vibration, against cycles since installation for that engine;
— cruise performance deviation from nominal for EGT, fuel flow, HP spool speed (N2), and LP/HP spool vibration, plotted against cycles since installation.

These are updated daily and stored in databases for online access by users if required; this eliminates unwanted production of printouts.

Further developments

Beyond the original variables described above, consideration is being given to other features:

Fan rotor imbalance measurement for large turbofans. This can be deduced from phase/amplitude analysis of the vibration sensors. Quantifying the error can provide maintenance workers with an actual mass/position correction before they see the engine, and avoid the need to remove engines for test bed runs. Implementation of this option faces some problems related to knowledge of the fan balance bolts and their effects, and obtaining consistent results from the vibration readings taken during cruise conditions.

Engine module test analysis. The program can analyse the data acquired during test bed runs of an engine. This can be used to establish the air flow characteristics and efficiencies of modules (LP compressor, HP compressor, etc.) into which modern engines are split for maintenance purposes. The intention is to correlate these results with build data from engine workshops for the same modules, to gain a better understanding of the working tolerances required.

Variable stator vane (VSV) tracking. Air mass flow into the engine is trimmed by the VSV settings. These have been adjusted on the ground, according to rules provided in maintenance manuals. Examination of actual performance during flight can establish whether the VSV is correctly rigged in relation to the other engine controls to achieve best performance margins under all conditions. The VSV should operate in a progressive way as the engine speed varies, and this is sometimes difficult to confirm on the ground.

TURBINE ENGINE OIL MONITORING

Introduction

Oil system monitoring for gas turbine engines can be of:

— oil system operation;
— oil debris;
— oil condition.

One or more of these may be performed in a particular implementation. The system used may be self-contained onboard the aircraft, or require additional ground equipment and analysis. Oil system monitoring is one element of an engine condition monitoring program.

History

Oil system operation monitoring is the oldest form of analysis. Simply by measuring oil pressure, temperature and quantity, it is possible to make useful inferences about the engine state. A filter blockage indicator is also a simple form of alert requiring further action. Debris monitoring by inspection of filters, special screens, and magnetic plugs also predates turbine engines. The technique of siting detector plugs in oil lines leading from critical bearings has proved particularly useful in turbine engines, but was also used on aircraft engines before the jet age.

Turbine engines used in aircraft have high rotational-shaft speeds, and run at high temperatures, using air taken from the compressor to cool the turbine discs. The oil is used to cool the shaft bearings, which may operate in hot parts of the engine. The thrust of a jet engine results from the difference between much larger forces produced by the compressor and turbine sections, acting in opposite directions. Thus turbine bearings are heavily loaded and deterioration can result in serious secondary damage if their working clearances are exceeded through wear.

Early methods of turbine engine oil-debris analysis relied on regular sampling of the filters for particles, by visual examination with or without microscopes. Certain failure modes produce distinctive particle size, shape and frequency, and an experienced inspector can confidently recommend action from these. Some operators leave the initial examination to a line mechanic, who may send the samples on to a specialist if unusual signs are apparent. Some operators adjust the frequency of requested oil filter inspection according to their concern about the engine or engine type.

The success of these early methods encouraged engine manufacturers to incorporate oil debris collectors in the design, making it easier to perform the inspection without oil loss, and removing some of the risks of contamination inherent in the process. Chip collectors of various kinds, magnetic and electric, became common features in turbine engines.

These methods are capable of detecting particles exceeding about 50 microns (1,000 microns = 1 mm). If measurements below 10 microns are desired, a spectrometric oil analysis program (SOAP) is used. Recently, more elaborate methods including direct measurement of debris and signalling of results have been developed, such as quantitative debris monitoring (QDM). These are of particular interest to helicopter operators, since transmission monitoring is a vital requirement for safety in rotorcraft.

Benefits

Oil system monitoring has several advantages, in prevention of engine failures, life development of engines, operational flexibility in maintenance, but it also has running costs to be considered. For large, costly engines this is not a factor, but operators of smaller powerplants may only be able to justify the simpler systems. Of course, if the oil analysis is very successful in anticipating potential failures, the owners of the engines may have to be reminded of this. One problem encountered by airline managers is that the need for a monitoring program may become apparent when it is too late to implement one, so expensive failures may occur which could have been averted with foresight. A basic oil analysis program which can be quickly upgraded as necessary may be regarded as a useful form of insurance against future problems.

Oil system operation monitoring

Oil pressure measurement is the original form of monitoring, dating from piston engines. Oil pressure as such is not so important in turbine engines, but it is still useful to know, and low oil pressure warning indicators in the cockpit are a mandatory requirement for aircraft.

Oil temperature is important for turbine engines, not just as a sign of engine distress, but also because overheating can alter the lubricating properties of the oil and permanently damage seals. Temperature sensors may be located at different points in the oil flow, so that outlet from a bearing or oil cooler may be monitored. It is common in most engines to use the oil cooler as a fuel heater, so reducing the risk of petroleum wax particles in the fuel blocking the finer parts of the fuel control unit.

Oil quantity is measured because some faults in turbine engine internal cooling systems can cause increases in oil consumption, the oil mist not being recovered in the circulation. Seal failure can also lead to rapid loss of oil. Monitoring may be done by looking at a dipstick before every flight, or by internal contents gauges.

Filter bypass indicators are provided as alerts. Oil filters are designed to unseat if they become so badly clogged that flow rate is inadequate, on the principle that dirty oil is better than none at all. A bypass indicator should require immediate maintenance action to establish the cause. Some airworthiness regulations specify an impending bypass indicator, set to trip just below the filter bypass level. Both of these may be either cockpit indicators or mechanical devices visible on the engine.

Oil debris monitoring

Debris monitoring takes many forms, from visual examination only to quantitative assessments with trend estimation. The objective is to detect failure modes which develop rapidly, a requirement needing skill and good organisation — there is no value in identifying the failure of an engine which is already on its way to the shop. Prompt detection and reaction are essential.

In conditions of full lubrication, failure of rolling-contact bearings is typically by 'spalling' or pitting induced by surface fatigue. This produces large particles in the 100 to 1,000 micron range, easily visible and of distinctive appearance. In other conditions, involving point contact, much smaller particles result and abrasive or adhesive wear may occur. Bearing skidding produces very small particles, below 25 microns, and leads to rapid wear if not arrested.

Failure modes by wear can thus be detected from oil debris monitoring. It is important to realise that fatigue failure modes give little indication of wear in advance, so these methods are of little use.

Onboard debris monitoring has become more common with the development of sensors and processors capable of providing such indications. Devices used or proposed include:

— magnetic chip collector;
— electric chip detector;
— pulsed electric chip detector;
— screen-type full-flow debris monitor;
— centrifugal debris separator;
— quantitative debris monitor;
— electro-optical debris monitor;
— inductive debris monitor;
— indicating screen;
— X-ray fluorescence monitor;
— on-line ferrograph;
— degaussing chip detector;
— capacitative debris monitor.

Some of these are still in the experimental stage, however they may appear in production systems.

Ground-based debris monitoring techniques use regular sampling of oil and laboratory analysis. Examples include:

— spectrometric analysis;
— quantification and analysis of magnetic chip debris;
— filter analysis;
— ferrography;
— colorimetric oil analysis;
— radioactive tagging;
— X-ray spectrophotometer;
— scanning electron microscope.

It is apparent that some of these require specialist staff and equipment to perform. Many operators are unlikely to have these, and the work may be performed more effectively by contractors.

Oil condition monitoring

This is physical or chemical analysis of the oil to determine its condition and suitability for continued use. Aircraft turbine engine oils are 'synthetic', that is, a blend of petroleum chemicals rather than refined petroleum with additives, as for automotive oils. Damage by oxidisation, acidity, fuel dilution, solids, depletion, can alter the properties. Assessment of these again requires specialist laboratory work best done by contractors.

General

Oil analysis system design must consider many factors:

— cost/benefit analysis for operation and savings;
— failure modes likely to be identified;
— reliability of detection;
— engine design and construction;
— oil system transport of debris;
— extent of oil filtration;
— criteria for engine removal;
— ease of use in service;
— training of maintenance staff;
— supply of equipment;
— reference documents.

With systems used onboard aircraft, consideration should also be given to:

— sensors and transducers;
— operating environment effects — engines are harsh;
— weight and reliability of equipment;
— accessibility for retrieval and maintenance;
— inspection requirements;
— location of warnings or displays;
— interfaces, signal conditioners, and connectors;
— built-in test equipment.

For ground-base systems, it is important to consider:

— sampling methods and equipment;
— frequency of sampling;
— response time;

— cost of special equipment and staff;
— oil replacement;
— calibration.

Oil system considerations

The onboard debris monitors rely on the transport characteristics of the oil system, and can react to particles of much wider size range than the oil filter can process. They are therefore sited ahead of the filter. Some electronic sensors cannot withstand hot oil temperatures.

Sensor design and location should recognise the transport characteristics; the more debris captured, the greater chance of detection. Installing more sensors to detect more failure modes will increase cost and may reduce the chance of detecting an individual failure.

Another factor to be considered is the degree of filtration demanded in the engine. Requirements are becoming stricter because of the effects on bearing life, leading to finer filters. At levels below 5 micron particle size, some techniques described above cannot be used effectively.

TURBINE ENGINE VIBRATION MONITORING IN AIRCRAFT

Introduction

Airborne vibration monitoring (AVM) equipment is fitted to most transport aircraft. A vibration monitoring system comprises the hardware, data, and analysis procedures. Engine vibration monitoring can be one of the systems used in engine condition monitoring or it may be the only such system. Ground-based engine vibration analysis systems also exist, commonly as part of test bed instrumentation.

Engine vibration systems first appeared in the later piston engines, and then on early civil jet engines. At that time they were regarded as optional extras, because of the difficulty in providing much onboard analysis. This stemmed partly from the lack of suitable miniaturised electronic components and from the harsh electrical and mechanical environment in which they operated.

Gas turbine engines used in aircraft have rotor shafts carrying the discs or drums to which the compressor or turbine blades are fitted. These can run at very high rotational speeds, especially in small engines, so that loss of dynamic balance by wear or damage can produce cyclic loads on parts of the engine, leading to further damage if not checked. Turbine engine components, such as blades, which can affect running balance are weighed and graded before assembly and the complete engine or modules are statically and dynamically balanced at overhaul. It is not possible to eliminate imbalance with realistic working tolerances, so all engines will exhibit some vibration; a judgement has to be made about an acceptable level of vibration when calibrating the system and its instruments, particularly those in the cockpit. Early designs of AVM systems earned a reputation for unreliability from flight crews, and efforts were made by manufacturers to improve transducer and processor accuracy.

Engine faults which vibration monitoring can detect are:

— blade loss or partial loss;
— blade mounting disturbance;
— missing rotor parts, such as bolts, etc.;
— blade coating delamination;
— bearing misalignment or wear;
— oil or debris in rotors;
— reheat system instability (military aircraft).

Typical AVM system

Vibration transducers are usually small accelerometers using piezoelectric effects. One or more are mounted in the engine and connected to electronic amplifier/filter units which feed flight deck instruments calibrated in arbitrary units. In a modern civil aircraft, vibration isolation of the engines makes alternative instrumentation essential for detecting engine distress. This may be sudden loss of blades as a result of ingestion damage, or resonance effects combined with wear. Most engines will continue to give acceptable thrust even with damage that would be visible on ground inspection, but the handling characteristics may be adversely affected.

System design

Specification of an AVM system should take account of the expected costs and benefits, the data to be acquired and its use, and the maintenance of the system. The temptation to over-specify in the expectation of detecting otherwise unknown faults should be weighed against providing for further development if experience shows it is needed.

Among the factors to be considered are:

Signal quality. This will depend on the positioning, mounting, and connection of the transducer; it should obviously be capable of measuring the actual vibration of critical engine parts.

Transducer type. These may be displacement, velocity or acceleration types. The most widely used now is the accelerometer type based on piezoelectric effects in ceramic or crystal material. This design is robust and capable of withstanding the engine environment. Directional sensitivity is an important consideration in transducer selection, as is the absence of temperature-dependent effects.

Signal transmission. The transducer is a high-impedance device, which presents difficulties in sending signals over long distance. Low noise cable is presently used in preference to a pre-amplifier near the engine. Circuit design minimises interference effects.

Connectors. These should be as few as possible up to the first signal-conditioning unit, though this can make maintenance difficult. Couplings should be secure against movement.

Signal processing methods used include integration of the acceleration to estimate velocity and then again for displacement. Displacement is useful at low frequencies, velocity at higher, and vibration at high frequencies. Rotor speed is usually in the frequency range appropriate to velocity. Filtering is also applied to the signal, especially when the engine itself is of constant speed operation. Otherwise different filters may be used to remove known vibration sources.

Tracking-filter based systems

In this design, the filter pass frequencies are dynamically tied to the rotor speeds. A narrow band filter is used. Tachometer signals should be sufficiently accurate to provide the required tracking. A recent development is to use phase reference signals in addition to tachometer tracking, so that fan-rotor imbalance may be measured without resorting to ground running or test bed use of the engine.

Responsibilities

A successful vibration monitoring system requires understanding of its capabilities by all users, and co-ordination of their actions. Operators should ideally select systems suitable for their needs and explain the significance to flight-deck crew and ground engineers. Development of a company policy for monitoring vibration levels, from the engine workshop to the aircraft, and reacting to identified events, is also important.

LIFE USAGE MONITORING

Introduction

Life usage monitoring of engine parts has long been recognised as important for aircraft safety and economics. Turbine engine parts are susceptible to failure modes generated by cyclic mechanical and thermal stress (fatigue, shock), and by sustained stress and temperature (creep). These effects are observed in laboratory tests, from which the requirements for safe operation are developed.

The original methods of life usage used cycle counting as a measurement, a cycle usually being a single flight in civil use or a more complex definition in military use. This was then related to expected stresses in an average operating profile to calculate the life used, and projected forward to the time or date expected for replacement. Major engine components have been shown to exhibit more consistent failure-age distributions than other aircraft components, but there is still some scatter in the data, so high safety factors are used when stating the maximum life.

These methods, though conservative and safe, may lead to loss of potential engine life in cases where the actual operations differ from the assumed. Development of technology capable of measuring inflight stresses more frequently, has led to the current interest in direct calculation of life usage.

General

The failure of an engine part may be caused by cumulative damage resulting from cyclic or steady stresses produced by rotational speed, temperature, or pressure. This damage affects the microstructure of the material and is not easily verified by non-destructive testing, therefore some form of preventive action is necessary. In any case, there is no form of restoration other than remanufacture of the part, so replacement at some time is inevitable.

During design, the effects of stress on the engine parts are investigated by theoretical analysis, component testing in rigs, extreme tests, and full-scale tests to represent actual use. From these a relation between the applied stress and achieved life is built up, which can be used to estimate the expected life in use when the stresses in use

Plate 18 Rolls-Royce RB-211 engine build

are measured to a sufficient degree of accuracy. The advantage of this method should be that changes in the operating environment are immediately reflected in counts of the life accumulated.

Maintenance systems of this kind, which result in each part having its own replacement decision, place heavy demands on the parts management system. The older approach, in which every part in a module, assembly or engine received rework or replacement irrespective of its condition, was easy to administer with nothing more than paperwork for the engine build. The modern approach of having interchangeable parts and modules requires a disciplined attitude to engine management. It is possible, for instance, to produce serviceable engines in the short term by switching modules to use up the remainder of lives, but since no actual restoration is being done the eventual result of this is a shortage of available engines. Another consideration is that if a quality fault were to be discovered in a particular part or process, then all other items of the same batch are suspect and must be located and examined quickly. Without a computer-based parts management system this is a daunting task for an operator. It follows that all life-limited parts must be identified with serial numbers that survive in use.

Parts classification

Certain engine parts are critical and may therefore be life-limited if it can be shown that deterioration is age related. These will be identified early in the design by the manufacturer, and the operator must adhere to the recommendation. Parts essential to safe flight are classed as critical life-limited. If analysis shows a part is not essential to flight safety but may cause considerable secondary damage, it is classed as non-critical life-limited. Rotating parts subject to low cycle fatigue (LCF) are nearly always critical life-limited. This applies whatever the use of the engine, but criteria for non-critical parts may vary between single-engine and multi-engined aircraft, since a precautionary inflight shutdown is less serious with several engines.

Even when the life has been determined, the part should be regularly inspected for signs of cracking, corrosion, wear or damage.

Failure of life-limited parts

Life-limited parts are those likely to fail for predictable reasons, owing to metallurgical phenomena such as fatigue or creep. Other causes of failure may be damage, wear, corrosion, negligence, or defective manufacture. Considering the first group:

Low cycle fatigue (LCF). This is normally due to repeated high stress applications within the material's elastic limit, leading to strain hardening and failure. This occurs usually in under 50,000 cycles, a cycle being one from zero stress to maximum and back again. LCF stresses can be caused by centrifugal, torsional or pressure loads, or by thermal gradients. Rotating parts such as shafts or discs are susceptible to LCF, though inertia forces can affect non-rotating parts sufficiently to cause LCF. Military engines experience more LCF usage than civil, because of more frequent high-power throttle action in military missions.

High cycle fatigue (HCF). This is caused by lower stress amplitudes than LCF, therefore failure usually occurs above 50,000 cycles. HCF loads may be caused by vibration, and are more difficult to predict in advance of operational use. Usage measurement for HCF is not so advanced as with LCF, so it is not currently implemented in engine monitoring systems.

Thermal fatigue. This is induced by temperature differences in the material, causing internal stresses. Rapid engine-shaft speed changes will cause this, exposing some parts to sudden increases in gas temperature. Thermal fatigue problems are one of the limitations of non-metallic materials, which otherwise have excellent properties for use in engines. Thermal fatigue occurs during engine starts or large power demands.

Creep. This is a time-dependent effect; long cruise periods can result in creep failure. Exposure to prolonged stresses at high temperature causes changes in the microstructure of the alloy which are irreversible. At temperatures near the creep limit, very small changes will result in large distortions of the material, so measurement and control of engine temperatures is important in ensuring long life and estimating usage.

Engine life prediction

Failure of critical engine parts may be dangerous, and for single-engined military aircraft it may cause loss of the aircraft. Accurate life prediction and usage measurement are therefore important. Modern engine parts are very expensive, however, and there is considerable interest in extracting the maximum safe use from them. This requires a good understanding of the failure mechanism, and the development of algorithms to assess life usage; some of these methods are patented.

In the design, a manufacturer will estimate the typical flight profile to predict the life. In operation, a usage monitoring system should record actual events and calculate the life, which may be different. This implies that operator's specifications for new engine types should take into account this possibility by careful definition of what is required. Any workshop forecasting method used by the operator will have to obtain and predict the data needed for usage monitoring, if it is not directly related to measures such as flight time or landings.

When an accurate usage monitoring system is available, the possibility of optimising engine parts' lives can be considered. Operation at reduced power settings will prolong engine life, but may increase aircraft operating costs by extra time spent at less fuel-efficient altitudes or speeds. Knowing the exchange between these factors, an optimum engine derating strategy can be adopted for a particular pattern of operations.

The algorithms used to calculate low cycle fatigue vary from largely empirical ones, derived from experience, to more theoretical ones based on material science and physics of failure. Some of them are built into the data analysis system and remain unknown to the operator, who simply receives a 'fraction used' readout. The broad principle of LCF estimation is to convert a stress-time history into cycles of loading and then refer to a 'damage map' for the material to convert the effect of the cycles into life usage. This can be performed entirely inside an airborne instrument with modern microelectronics, so that a direct readout is obtained.

Thermal fatigue estimation can be performed in a similar way to mechanical LCF counting, by processing temperature history instead of stress.

Creep life estimation requires knowledge of the stress and temperature history experienced by the part. This is possible, but does not seem to be in such widespread use as LCF estimation, possibly because creep is not a limiting factor for most operators.

Limit exceedance recording is possible with a continuous engine monitoring system. This includes shaft overspeed, turbine temperatures above limits, hot starts, compressor surges, any of which may result in engine damage and require action.

The engine parameters measured for life usage are those already required for other purposes, such as engine handling and flight control. There is thus no need for additional transducers, but additional signal processing may be needed.

Validation

When a life-usage monitoring system enters service, it should be validated for the usage algorithm's ability to measure actual use, and for the monitoring system's ability to measure and calculate the life used. This is similar to other certification processes involving automation and data analysis, and may continue after the aircraft enters service.

Data management

A system for relating the engine-life usage measured to the control of engine parts must exist. This should maintain a database of all engine parts and possess the ability to update their life usage and to provide maintenance workshops with forecasts of workload and the means to schedule work according to priorities decided by management. It is unlikely that forecasts will always predict actual events, so rescheduling of work in progress to meet revised production targets is a desirable feature. In most engine rework there is some slack and very few parts are critical to the whole engine being completed on time; resources can be allocated to these as needed.

Benefits

The correct application of engine usage monitoring can result in reduced maintenance costs, with higher reliability and safety. Better knowledge of the engine fleet status and more flexibility for adjusting plans can improve the operator's reaction to changes in aircraft schedules. Feedback to manufacturers and provisioning of spare parts should be more precise.

CURRENT CAPABILITIES OF NDT — A SERVICE OPERATOR'S VIEW

Aircraft

The RAF operates many aircraft types, having a wide range of aircraft ages, from 1930s designs (BoB Memorial Flight) to the latest carbon fibre composite (CFC) aircraft — Harrier GR5; for NDT purposes, these may be divided into three main groups:

Old aircraft. The aircraft in around half the RAF's front line squadrons are over 15 years old. This is a growing NDT task, but the faults are usually easy to detect.

Young aircraft. Delivery plans in hand will soon provide many front line squadrons with aircraft under 5 years old. Where these aircraft have optimised structural design and small critical crack lengths, NDT has to detect them.

Advanced aircraft. Future examples are the European Fighter Aircraft (EFA). This and other new types, using new materials and advanced engines, will place severe demands on NDT.

This range of aircraft requires the RAF to develop many NDT techniques. The organisation responsible for this is the Central Servicing Development Establishment (CSDE) at RAF Swanton Morley, Norfolk. Working in association with the aircraft manufacturers, it produces over 100 new techniques a year.

Military operations

Maintenance problems generated by military operations are different from those of civilian flying. The flying rate and maintenance hours taken by the RAF are lower than airline figures, but the aircraft are flown to higher stress levels and have to stay in service for many years. Operations and maintenance can be carried out from very different sites, such as conventional airfields, dispersed airfields or overseas stations. Central fixed bases as used by airlines cannot be counted on. Aircraft maintenance in the RAF is usually based on flying hours. Shorter maintenance, at about 75 hours, is done at first line, which is the operating unit/squadron. Deeper maintenance, which includes major rectification, is usually carried out at the unit's station by the second line organisation, which has the necessary equipment and skills. Third line maintenance also exists for major overhauls; there are very few stations equipped to do this, and such work may also be contracted to manufacturers.

First line maintenance may have to be done outdoors, even in bad weather. Second line work requires hangars and their facilities. NDT tasks have to be performed in both levels; therefore portability of equipment is considered essential, so its design has to be compromised to achieve this. Access in some modern aircraft with small confined equipment bays is difficult, though more consideration has been given to maintainability in recent RAF aircraft. NDT techniques in the RAF are developed for specific problems; general scanning for unknown faults is not usually done except to assess corrosion. Events leading to an NDT solution occur in fatigue tests, in-service incidents, and manufacturer's alerts.

The organisation of NDT in the RAF is by regional teams. Each team is responsible for several local stations, which may operate different aircraft types.

Qualification of staff

Work is carried out by trained NDT technicians; these are drawn from the more experienced staff who have the requisite qualifications to understand the nature of the work to be done. Training is provided by CSDE, followed by a qualification period working under supervision. Eventually the RAF NDT technician works without supervision; therefore a high level of personal responsibility is expected. Separate inspection is not used. Civilian NDT technicians are also employed and trained similarly. For simple tasks, station personnel may be used. An unfortunate consequence of this selection and training process is that many RAF NDT technicians qualify in their last few years of service, so the return on training investment is soon lost. The new national certification scheme, the Personnel Certification in NDT (PCN), is supported by the RAF.

Techniques

The main NDT techniques used in the RAF are:

— visual aids;
— magnetic;
— penetrant;
— eddy current;
— ultrasonic;
— radiography.

These are well-known techniques in the aircraft industry. Other newer techniques, such as thermography, are studied by CSDE as possible solutions to specific problems. Methods which require a large amount of calibration are generally difficult to implement in a Service environment.

Detection limits

The minimum detectable fault size is of interest to aircraft designers and operators. This depends on the location and type of fault. Cracks at the order of 0.1 mm can be detected by magnetic methods, obviously in ferrous materials only. 1 mm scale cracks are detectable by eddy current methods. Slightly larger sizes, about 2 mm, can be detected by ultrasonic probes. These figures all apply to alloys traditionally used in aircraft construction. For carbon fibre composites (CFC), an objective has been set to detect 20 mm faults at first line and 6 mm faults at second line. This is expected to be possible with ultrasonic equipment used by trained personnel. Techniques suitable for use by local staff are being developed; aircraft such as the Harrier GR5, which have to operate from dispersed airfields, are a particular problem.

A common problem with using NDT is the difficulty of detecting small cracks arising at stress raisers such as bolt holes, corners, section changes. Fastener holes are a very high proportion (80 per cent) of the problems in metal structures. Another difficulty is the need for concentration by the operator in repetitive tasks, an example being the need to inspect thousands of rivets on a wing. Engines not designed with

NDT inspection in mind can also require prolonged investigation to examine all sites. Skills are maintained by using calibrated specimens to reassure technicians of the equipment's capability.

Future developments

Future demands for the NDT functions are expected to be:

New materials. Non-metallic structures using CFC require different detection techniques to be explored, and an understanding of the acceptable damage limits to be gained by theory and experience. New high-strength alloys used in engines may have very small critical crack sizes not detectable by present technology.

New designs. Structures are now being designed and manufactured to much better weight optimisation and manufacturing tolerance than before. This means that excess material once used as a safety factor is no longer provided, and faults must be found quickly to ensure integrity. The use of 'damage tolerant' philosophy in design recognises that probability of detection must be allowed for. New manufacturing methods such as superplastic forming may introduce failure modes not seen before. Increasing use of anti-corrosion protection coatings required to meet low life-cycle cost targets may inhibit current NDT techniques.

On-condition maintenance. Progress in the elimination of unnecessary work depends on suitable measures of health being developed. NDT is expected to be a significant factor in this.

Economics. NDT itself must be sufficiently cheap and reliable to justify its use in place of preventive maintenance, routine replacement, or other simpler but less scientific methods. The high cost of modern aircraft parts, and the long lives expected of them, favour the use of NDT.

Flight safety. The primary objective is to make aircraft operation safer for everyone, not just the RAF but also the communities where they operate.

HELICOPTER MAINTENANCE

Introduction

Helicopters pose some special problems for aircraft operation and maintenance, for example:

Engine failure at certain phases of flight is extremely critical. This is reflected by rating the emergency power in a different way from that used in fixed-wing aircraft.

Vibration affects components and structure in a helicopter more extensively than in fixed-wing aircraft. Latest helicopter designs have much better vibration isolation than older ones, but the problem still exists in the machinery that generates vibration.

Low altitude and over water operations, characteristic of many helicopter users, increase the exposure to atmospheric turbulence, ingestion damage and corrosion.

These problems have been recognised by the industry and attempts have been made to deal with them. One method is the use of health and usage monitoring system (HUMS), made possible by improvements in instrumentation and processing with digital systems. Concern at the accident rate experienced in civil helicopter use led to the study and report known as the UK CAA Helicopter Airworthiness Review Panel (HARP), in 1984 (CAP 491). This recommended a series of modifications to existing helicopters, and a further programme of research for the future, including condition monitoring.

Because the transmission from engines via gearboxes to rotors is a vital part of any modern helicopter, interest in gearbox health monitoring began early. This usually took the form of oil analysis for signs of particles, by removable magnetic chip detectors or filter inspection. More recent examples are 'quantitative debris monitors' (QDM) which can signal a debris count to cockpit instruments or a flight recorder without the need for routine inspection. Vibration analysis has also been tried for early warning of defects. One useful way of reducing vibration at source is to improve the main rotor blade balancing and tracking, and several automatic test devices are now marketed to perform this. Rotor maintenance itself has been greatly simplified by designs using elastic supports and hinges instead of shafts and bearings, so that wear of sliding surfaces is avoided. Hollow, gas pressurised, rotor blades can be fitted with indicators to reveal the existence of cracks.

Health usage monitoring system

A HUMS requires instruments, a flight data recorder (FDR), and signal-processing equipment. The instrumentation may be extra to that already fitted for flight use, and the processing may be done onboard for use by the crew or maintenance engineers, or in ground computers for use at base or by airworthiness authorities. Trial programmes have been conducted by some UK manufacturers and operators in cooperation with the UK CAA, with the objective of meeting certification in 1991. This includes the requirement to fit crash-protected FDRs to helicopters, which are small vehicles in comparison with fixed-wing aircraft required to carry accident recorders. As with the original fixed-wing requirement, operators see an associated health-monitoring function as a way of recovering the cost of fitting mandatory FDRs.

According to experience reported by one trial operator (Bristow), 85 per cent of serious helicopter incidents and 55 per cent of accidents were likely to be detectable by their HUMS. Accident rates for old helicopters fitted with HUMS are expected to reduce by a half or less, while current helicopters so fitted would have still lower accident rates. The full benefit of designing this into new helicopters would produce the safest result of all. These estimates assume that advanced vibration analysis would be 95 per cent effective in detecting transmission-fatigue failures, and that present helicopters have rotor systems with a damage-tolerant rating of 50 per cent of that possible with future designs. The target helicopter fatal-accident rate of 0.5 per million flying hours would be near the recent experience of fixed-wing civil aircraft, at 0.3 per million flying hours.

Installation of HUMS would enable on-condition maintenance of helicopter parts to work more effectively; previously the obvious existence of fatigue-related use required hard-time maintenance.

AN INVESTIGATION OF AIRCRAFT INSPECTION

Introduction

CAA Paper 85013 'Reliability of In-service Inspection of Transport Aircraft Structures' (1985) describes a study of the reliability of structural inspection with particular emphasis on the influence of human factors on the performance of inspection. Information was obtained from visits to operators, examination of mandatory occurrence reports, a questionnaire circulated among selected aircraft-operating companies, and by observation of shop-floor practice. The report contains a number of conclusions and makes recommendations for improving inspection methods.

The report explains that structural inspection is mainly intended to reveal the cracks and corrosion characteristic of the ageing in aircraft. Location of the defects is therefore essential, and visual means are still the most common way of doing this.

Factors cited as relevant to the reliability of inspection are:

— the large size of structures to be inspected;
— the time available to inspect the required areas;
— the conditions under which inspections take place, the attitude of the inspector, the background knowledge of the inspector and the organisational structure;
— the lack of defect-location aids away from main bases;
— geographical locations which may involve extremes of climate;
— local conditions such as poor access, or bad lighting;
— commercial or market pressures requiring aircraft to be operational quickly.

Although there are many techniques for assessing cracks and corrosion once detected, there is still no easy way of finding small cracks in large structures. The report therefore concludes that improvement in inspection reliability is best obtained by improving the efficiency and working conditions of inspectors.

In their work, the investigators reviewed current inspection practices, primarily on transport-category aircraft, by discussion with inspectors and operators and by circulation of a questionnaire to inspection and quality-control staff. A survey of mandatory occurrence reports (MOR) was also made to see the extent of significant structural damage and to estimate the inspection problem.

Conclusions and recommendations

A summary of these is given here, to show the nature of inspection, the kind of problems faced by inspectors, and the reaction of independent observers to the process.

Personal factors
Eyesight

The vision of the inspector is considered of prime importance. The questionnaire revealed that 50 per cent of the sample of inspectors could not read typescript over 4 ft (1.2 m) away. The effects of this in restricted areas, where close inspection directly opposite the part is difficult, could be serious.

The investigators contacted the Association of Optical Practitioners in London, who informed them of ways to test an inspector's eyesight regularly. Appropriate vision-screening equipment is available at a cost; the report suggested the CAA might use this. The Association suggested that a set of vision requirements be tabulated for inspectors, who could then be made responsible for obtaining a yearly certificate of vision. This would be covered under the NHS. The Association has a committee with much experience of formulating vision requirements for such bodies as the Police and Fire Service.

Motivation and attitude

The report considered that the motivation of the inspector was rarely, if ever, a factor adversely affecting reliability, because of dedication to the task and job satisfaction. The inspector's attitude could be affected by factors such as bodily comfort on the job, home matters, operator attitudes, wages, health.

The authors' experience and the questionnaire answers indicate that, as with motivation, there was little or no effect on reliability. The reason for this seemed to be that any factors adversely affecting the inspector's attitude towards his job have the effect of increasing his inspection time and/or his defect-reporting rate, with consequent extra cost to the operator. The gulf between aircrew and ground-staff conditions and remuneration was quoted as a major cause of dissatisfaction. It was suggested that the operator could alleviate this to some extent by providing comparable facilities, such as crewrooms and workshops.

Training and experience

There were several comments on training, with indications that, on the whole, the approach to engineering training was first class in the aircraft industry, being a good balance between knowledge of engineering as a whole and knowledge of particular aircraft.

The authors felt that the abandonment of 'with type rating' could lead to a lessening of inspection standards, and a lengthening of the period during which the inspector gains his experience, because of the lack of formal training. Examinations on types were regarded as a better way for the inspector to see the total picture in a way that does not occur if experience is gained piecemeal.

Comments were also made, in the report, that growth of experience might be limited unless the working inspector is kept up to date on inspection and maintenance happenings elsewhere in the industry.

This would involve feedback of the effects of an inspector's own major-defect reports, such as the eventual effect of informing the manufacturer, quality-assurance reaction, schedule amendment, and explanation of the severity of the incident. A system of regular refreshment, for the knowledge required, was recommended, apart from the training requirements. Demonstration of new equipment for both inspection and engineering was mentioned. This might help rid the industry of its poor torches, mirrors and other tools.

Feedback

The efficiency of an inspector depends on his basic training and his subsequent experience. The latter increases in time by the number of defects he sees. The quality of his judgement in any one situation depends not only on the times he has seen it before but on the reinforcement he has received through feedback from those concerned with the subsequent analysis.

The report commented that there seemed to be little effort to inform the inspector of the results of this analysis. Although discussion of the defect with the foreman of quality-control staff occurred at the time, reinforcement of his experience by comparing it with, say, the manufacturer's report was felt to be absent. An example quoted was the relative size of acceptable crack lengths in different parts of a structure, coupled with the inspector's opinion of their subsequent growth rate and the strength in each part.

Use of video equipment could be made for visual demonstration of inspection procedures. This would be especially useful where a procedure was difficult or lengthy to describe. In this way, an experienced inspector could demonstrate and spread skills more widely amongst others. Major faults are usually transmitted through the system rapidly, but small defects may eventually prove significant.

The investigators noted that more defect cards arose during minor checks taken with block hangar checks than when only the minor check was done. The conclusion was that rectification of minor defects was postponed. A system for warning about these was suggested, as with ADDs.

Inspector quality

The report concluded that the quality of inspection was not affected by wage rates, promotion prospects or bonus payments. However, there was evidence of a gradual decrease in relative status and rates which might, if prolonged, lead to a lowering in inspector quality by encouraging departure from the industry and, worse still, discouraging the brighter school leaver from coming into the industry. On-going training should be the rule rather than the exception. Providing each inspector with more formal data concerning his own operator's maintenance problems and those of others, would be of benefit throughout the industry.

The interest in the aircraft meant that the inspector was responsive to the CAA, and this independence should be fostered by contact. Unease was expressed at the gradual transfer of power from the CAA to the operator, as a possible source of conflict of interest. The authors noted some anxiety about the trend towards combined inspector/supervisor functions, though this might be expected in organisations still working with these functions segregated.

Workplace factors

Access

There were frequent complaints about access. Poor access can either entail difficulty in getting into the position for inspection (primary access) or difficulty seeing or feeling an area when in the best position possible (secondary access).

Ideally, custom-built staging should be provided for inspectors, giving primary access to all areas. In practice a mixture of scaffolding, planks and towers is often all that exists. The use of specialised lifts or hoists is the best way to get access if custom staging is not available. Easy primary access must reduce error, for the inspector is left free with both hands to inspect. If he is concerned mostly with holding on or balancing, it is impossible for him to push or pull fasteners and structure to the desired extent.

Secondary access problems can be caused by insufficient panel removal, lack of headroom or width, poor component design and location or poor inspection tools. Little can be done about the first three on current aircraft, but the tools can be improved. Bad access costs time, and shortening of inspection time, with consequent lesser coverage, especially in area checks. Improving access involves major costs or redesign, and the immediate cost may not be acceptable. However, the improvement in inspection and turnround time of aircraft being serviced should be offset against that cost.

Lighting

Adverse comments on lighting were also found. Sharpness of vision depends to some extent on the aperture, the size of the iris in the human eye; and this is directly dependent on the intensity of the light.

Good general lighting in the hangar is difficult where custom staging is not available because of the admission of aircraft into the hangar. It could therefore be possible to raise and lower strip lighting. Spotlight arrays were frequently seen but looked unwieldy, and were used as a substitute for torches, being an aid mostly to primary access. Poor lighting reduces the inspector's concentration and may induce minor headaches also.

Noise

For the majority of inspectors this has a major effect on their efficiency, reducing concentration, creating tension and shortening the effective inspection.

The prime sources of noise are auxiliary power units (APUs) and riveting guns. Better co-ordination with inspection periods, and choice of testing areas for APUs and other engines, would reduce this hazard, as would better noise-reduction and co-ordination of operating times of noisy equipment. An inspector inside a wing tank, on the outside of which there is a riveting gun operating, receives more noise than recommended in the HSE code of practice.

Equipment

Inspection equipment can be divided conveniently into two parts, electronic and manual.

In the electronic section, for example ultrasonic, eddy current, and X-ray, the systems are well chosen because of cost, regularly serviced and their sensitivities checked daily as a matter of course.

The manual systems are not serviced or calibrated in the same way. The equipment used by the inspector to aid the actual inspection is predominantly simple: a torch, a swivel mirror, a hand lens, a penknife and a coin (to check for delamination). With his eyes and fingers these 'tools' make up 99 per cent of the inspection kit. This excludes NDT equipment, as this is usually a specialist's job.

In general, the lens, knife, and coin do their job well; the torch and mirror less so. The light pattern of the average inspection torch is mottled in intensity, is dim and frequently has a dark centre. Coupled with torch cases that soften in hydraulic fluid or break if dropped, it is a poor display. The mirror is often too small (except for very awkward access), of poor reflecting ability (due to dirt, cracks, worn coating, etc.), and frequently has a loose swivel.

The eye—mirror—torch is the spearhead of the inspection process. Critical structure is, by the very nature of aircraft design, not often on the surface but buried in skin, cables, pipes, control rods, sensors, pumps, actuators, and so on. Good secondary access by reflection is essential. A quality standard needs to be set for both the torch and the mirror (or a useful combination).

Safety

This is a contributory factor to inspection reliability in so far as a comfortable inspector is likely to do a more efficient job than one feeling in danger of falling or being fallen on. Insufficient attention is paid to primary access safety; one support at each end of a plank 6 m from the ground is not enough, and the absence of toe-boards seems to be common on scaffolding.

The absence of any swarf-control procedure during rivet removal causes surface scratching on structure and the possibility of mechanical-control blockage; the final inspections and functional checking procedures do not reveal the presence of old rivet heads or stems, which can shake into the wrong position during subsequent flights. Although wing and tailplane surfaces may be covered during work above them, this covering can subsequently be moved before that work is finished, in order to carry out a final inspection, or even by wind if the hangar door is opened.

Scheduling and paperwork
The Approved Maintenance Schedule

This is a document of great complexity, built up from many sources. The possibility of error in this process is self-evident and will exist in spite of the great and conscientious efforts directed towards it.

Simplicity of instructions should be aimed at in AMS documentation; writers should not rely on interpretation by inspectors. Some instructions and diagrams are difficult, or at least time-consuming, to decipher and should be simplified.

One such error, which was missed on at least three levels, is described in the report. Here, the AMS omitted the instruction to remove an access panel, and a grease nipple was missed resulting in a seized tailplane bearing. The greaser and inspector consequently failed to notice that one nipple to be greased was inaccessible. Their main error was that they considered the AMS to be infallible. Other AMS errors likely to occur, besides typographical errors, are due to maintenance planning departments failing to call up the procedure relevant to the check being performed.

The authors' opinion is that scheduling should be computerised whenever economically feasible. The main drawback can be access to information; therefore the presentation and recovery of data should be of prime consideration, as should be ease of modification of the schedule.

The work card system

This is the method by which the inspector receives his instructions. It is generally by a series of cards carrying explicit or general area-checks to be made.

Several minor problems could arise by misuse of the card system, such as loss of a card or a failure to check off master listing. Existing checks, if effectively applied, will mean that these will only result in inconvenience and cost to the operator. However, the loss of a page of the usual rough note book, or an interruption in work pattern to answer requests from personnel wanting information, could cause a memory failure.

Separation of the inspection and supervision roles, either by having separate personnel or by allocating 'supervision-free' periods, would go a long way towards preventing inaccurate reporting as well as helping preserve the concentration of the inspector. Only the difficulty of instituting such a step prevented the authors from making it an itemised recommendation.

Area check or explicit instructions

Throughout the investigation it was clear that there was some debate as to whether area checks were wholly valid. All major structural parts or joints are explicitly defined by schedule references but an area check implies looking at everything. It is obviously not desirable or necessary to explicitly define every pipe-clip, row of rivets, cable, pulley, and so on, to be inspected; but inspectors would like more highlighting of all components or structures that have caused trouble in the past, and not just the major problems; these get an SB or similar notice in any case.

Component history analysis and MOR searches will not highlight a cable which is always found to be frayed or a clip always broken. The individual inspector has not the time to report this sort of occurrence nor, perhaps, the collective knowledge that this minor fault is repetitive. A system does exist which highlights this sort of defect; it consists of waiting until the stores runs out of that item or repair kit. A better system, of short written notes, would help prevent this time-consuming type of error. The scheduling computer could be used for this; it could collate areas with the relevant defect, for easy display to future inspectors, in order of number of occurrences.

Structure sampling

Where basic aircraft structure is thought to be subject to low load or fatigue levels, structural sampling is permitted. Instead of inspecting the complete structure of each aircraft in an operator's fleet at a certain time, only a proportion of each aircraft structure will be inspected. The total inspection carried out on the aircraft in this sample will be equivalent to inspecting at least one whole aircraft by the end of the inspection period.

As an example, taken from a B720 AMS sampling programme, one item was to be inspected each 40,000 hours; therefore subsequent aircraft in the sample (5 aircraft) were to be inspected every 8,000 hours. The agreement reached with the CAA for this particular item is shown in Table 6.2.

Clearly there is an abnormally large interval between the penultimate and last inspections of the sample. Naturally, it is as aircraft get older that structural deterioration occurs more frequently and yet this is the point where, in this case, the inspection period is twice the average. Fortunately sampling by one operator is not the only cover the aircraft type has, and defects in any of a particular type are reported to the CAA and the manufacturer. Sampling schemes may not be possible with aircraft whose ages are too disparate. Some more thought by those most concerned with sampling statistics may be needed to ensure that type cover is sufficient to override fleet-cover inconsistencies such as this.

Table 6.2   B720 AMS sampling programme, extract

Aircraft	Flight hrs	Hrs since last inspection
5	42,993	—
1	50,219	7,226
2	58,859	8,640
3	59,869	1,010
4	66,581	6,712
5	82,993	16,412

Aircraft
Labelling

During the inspection task the inspector is frequently presented with an instruction to check, say, the area bounded by two bulkheads. These are numbered in the instructions and in the diagrams which, with some greater or lesser loss of time, the inspector can obtain.

When he gets to the aircraft, entry may be by a small access panel and the room to manoeuvre small. The inspector may not have inspected this area for some time and a reminder, such as numbering on the bulkhead, would reinforce the location identity. Similarly, critical structural areas might be labelled or even patch-coloured to ensure their being correctly located and identified at inspection time. The authors accept that most inspectors are very conversant with the type they are inspecting, but any relaxation of 'type rating' on the licence would increase inter-type mobility and consequently lessen the familiarity of the inspector.

Crack sizes and fracture mechanics

During analysis of the MOR, and then during the co-ordination of the questionnaire, much data was obtained concerning detectability of cracks. The questionnaire answers suggested that a flaw size of 0.25 in to 0.5 in (6 mm to 12 mm), depending on area condition, was on the limits of visual detectability. A histogram of flaws found during the MOR exercise shows a very similar result.

The scope of the report did not allow the authors to analyse the data more fully from each occurrence, and therefore the relationship between the crack size and the material geometry was not obtained. Had it been possible to extract this data easily, then some guide as to the seriousness of the cracks could have been made by relating these to the forces experienced by that part, through simple fracture-mechanics calculations. In general, the reply to a query sent to the manufacturer concerning a defective part or area consists solely of how to repair or replace it, and has no data on the criticality of this defect. Not only the large, dramatic failures should be assessed, but the lesser everyday defects, for it is these that may point to overstressing in the area and possibly more serious failure later.

Physical obstructions

In the design of the aircraft, pipework, cabling, trim, and other details should be placed so that primary structure is left accessible to the inspector wherever practicable. A frequent complaint in the questionnaire and interviews was of poorly designed, oil-soaked soundproofing and other insulation preventing easy access to structure, especially within passenger compartments. Excess use of anti-corrosive agent is also a problem and, being a penetrant and sealant, may disguise flaws. There is also still controversy on whether such agents act as crack-growth accelerators through a stress-corrosion mechanism.

Sealing of public areas

A frequent sight during maintenance is exfoliated material being replaced around the toilet or galley areas. Although some effort is made to seal these from the structure with plastic sheeting, it is clearly ineffective. It is possible that, instead of a floor support being exfoliated, it will be the pressure hull. A small exploratory study of the diffusion through various polymers of the relevant effluents and chemicals from these areas could be made.

Cleaning

Much is said throughout this report concerning cleaning of aircraft structure. Poor liaison between inspector and cleaner can result in defects being obliterated or harder to find. Initial corrosion products can be removed, or leaking cracks disguised. Shortage of time allotted in the programme for proper cleaning is a frequently heard complaint and it is the opinion of the authors that more detailed cleaning procedures should be laid down. Cleaning should be considered as a proper contributory factor to reliable inspection, and not as a job for the less skilled.

CHAPTER 7 CASE STUDIES

INTRODUCTION

The cases described here are extracted from aircraft accident reports. They were chosen for several reasons:

— They illustrate how the airworthiness and maintenance system functions, and how a breakdown in the process may lead to an accident.
— The accidents have influenced the design and maintenance philosophy of civil aircraft.

The Aloha accident concerned ageing aircraft, and, although this was already under review by the industry at the time of the accident, it put more urgency behind the drive to find solutions. The Lusaka accident showed that fail-safe structure has to be backed up by inspection methods capable of detecting deterioration, and was one of the events leading to the concept of damage-tolerant structural design, which recognises probability of detection as a factor to be considered.

The B747 cargo door incident did not in itself have much effect on the airworthiness system, but it shows the importance of communications in achieving safety through aircraft maintenance. It echoed the Paris DC10 accident in 1974, which was attributed to failure of the cargo door locking mechanism, exacerbated by a history of incorrect modification actions, and was preceded by a similar incident in the USA.

Accidents in which there is evidence that previous incidents gave warning of potential dangers in the equipment or operation: warnings that were apparently not followed up are usually seized on by the press as evidence of negligence; what isn't discussed is the volume of information that has to be filtered to find such evidence.

THE ALOHA INCIDENT

Summary and findings

On 28 April 1988, a Boeing 737-200 series aircraft operated by Aloha Airlines Inc. of Hawaii, flying at 24,000 ft (7,300 m), lost approximately 18 ft (5.5 m) of the upper fuselage structure between the rear of the cockpit and the region of the wing leading edge/fuselage junction. One flight attendant was lost overboard and presumed killed; seven passengers and one other flight attendant were seriously injured. The flight crew made an emergency descent to the nearest airfield and landed with no further casualties.

The aircraft had flown 35,496 hours and 89,680 landings prior to the accident; this was the second highest number of landings in the worldwide Boeing 737 fleet, although the short flights associated with these inter-island operations meant that a full cabin pressure of 7.5 psi (51.7 kPa) was not always attained (the world's highest landing cycle Boeing 737 was another Aloha Airlines aircraft).

The US National Transportation Safety Board (NTSB) investigation found that the probable cause of the accident was the failure of the airline's maintenance programme to detect the presence of significant disbonding and fatigue damage, which ultimately led to the failure of a lap joint and separation of the upper fuselage. Contributing factors cited in the report were:

— The failure of the airline management to supervise properly its maintenance force.
— The FAA's failure to evaluate properly the airline's maintenance programme and to assess its inspection and quality-control deficiencies.
— The FAA's failure to require an Airworthiness Directive inspection of all the lap joints, proposed by a Boeing alert service bulletin.
— The lack of a complete terminating action from Boeing or the FAA after the discovery of early production difficulties in the B737 cold-bond lap joint that resulted in low bond durability, corrosion and premature fatigue cracking.

Safety issues raised included:

— The quality and FAA surveillance of air-carrier maintenance programmes.
— The engineering design, certification and continuing airworthiness of the B737, with particular reference to multiple-site fatigue cracking of the fuselage lap joints.
— The human-factor aspects of maintenance and inspection for the continuing airworthiness of transport category aircraft, to include repair procedures and the training, certification and qualification of mechanics and inspectors.

Damage to the aircraft

A major portion of the upper-crown skin and structure separated in flight, causing an explosive decompression of the cabin. The damaged area extended from slightly aft of the main cabin entrance door, rearward about 18 ft (5.5 m) to the area just forward of the wings, and from the left side of the cabin at floor level to the right side at window level. The aircraft, valued at $5M, was damaged beyond repair and later broken up for scrap.

Fuselage separation area

The fuselage structure consists mainly of skin, frames and stringers. Skin panels are joined longitudinally at lap joints where the sheet metal of the upper skin panel overlaps the sheet metal of the lower skin panel by about 3 in (75 mm). At manufacture, this overlapped area was bonded and riveted with three rows of countersunk-head rivets.

The missing structure extended from body station (BS) 360 aft to about BS 540, and circumferentially from just above the floor on the left side of the aircraft, across the crown and down the right side to a position above the window belt. The structure from the top of the window belt to the floor on the right side was distorted severely and bent outward more than 90 degrees. The skin had peeled in this area leaving the frames, stringers and window forgings in place. On the left side, below the floor level, the skin had peeled off the structure in large V-shaped areas.

Five consecutive floor beams at BS420, 440, 460, 480, 500 were broken all the way through. Also, the adjacent floor beams at BS 400 and 500A were cracked nearly all the way through. The fractures and cracks were slightly to the left of the aircraft centreline. The frames at these same seven stations were broken on the left side, just below the floor beams. Most of the centre floor panels from BS 360 to BS 947 were displaced upwards, except in the overwing area. The right side cabin floor panels had not been displaced and little if any distress had occurred at the fastener locations for these panels.

However, on the left side of the aircraft between BS 400 and BS 500, along the inboard seat track, there was extensive floor panel displacement. The floor panels had displaced upwards and had reached their maximum displacement of 4 in (100 mm) at BS 440, matching the displacement of the broken floor beams.

A piece of fuselage section was trapped between the leading flap and the inboard side of the right engine strut, being the only significant part of the damaged area to be recovered. This piece had two skin repairs; it, and samples cut from the remaining fuselage skin, were sent to the Safety Board's materials laboratory for analysis.

Additional damage noted by the investigators included impact marks on the wing leading edges and tailplane, and dents on the fin leading edge. The inlet cowls of both engines were dented, and several first-stage fan blades of both engines were damaged. Fuselage remnants were found against the inlet guide vanes and embedded in the acoustic liner of the right engine. Some control cables leading to the engines from the cockpit were found to be broken; these prevented any power increase in the left engine. The cables were sent for examination.

The upper fuselage crown separation caused damage to overhead wiring, mostly for cabin services. Pressure lines to the flight data recorder (FDR) were broken, and the passenger oxygen distribution system was rendered unusable; the flight-crew oxygen system remained serviceable.

The aircraft's hydraulic system was not damaged; a landing-gear locking problem indicated to the crew during descent was found to be a light bulb failure. The pressurisation system was examined and found to be capable of normal operation.

In retrospect, it is remarkable that an aircraft with such extensive structural damage remained flyable, and that the crew was able to display such skill in landing under these difficulties.

Other related incidents

There had been one previous accident involving inflight structural failure of a Boeing 737 fuselage. A Far Eastern Air Transport Ltd 737-200 experienced a decompression and inflight breakup on 22 August 1981. The accident occurred near Sanyi, Miaoli, Taiwan, and was investigated by the Civil Aeronautics Administration (CAA), Taiwan. The Safety Board, Boeing, and the US FAA participated in the investigation. The CAA determined that the probable cause of the accident was:

> Extensive corrosion damage in the lower fuselage structures, and at a number of locations corrosion had penetrated through pits, holes and cracks. In addition there was the possible existence of undetected cracks because of the many pressurisation cycles (33,313 landings). Interaction of these defects, and the damage, had so deteriorated that rapid fracture occurred, with certain decompression and sudden break of passenger compartment floor beams and connecting frames, cutting control cables and electric wiring, leading to loss of power, loss of control, and inflight disintegration.

Lap joint design and bonding history

The Boeing 737 fuselage is built in four sections, nose, forward cabin (Section 43), mid-rear cabin, and tail. These sections are butt-joined at circumferential frames to form the complete fuselage. Section 43 forms the area where separation occurred. Each section is made of circumferential frames joined by longitudinal stringers covered by formed skin panels riveted to the underlying structure. Each skin panel in the upper part of Section 43 runs the entire length of 18 ft (5.5 m). Adjacent skin panels are joined longitudinally by overlapping the edge of the upper panel by about 3 in (75 mm) over the edge of the lower panel. This overlap joint is fastened with three rows of rivets and a bonding underneath the skin.

The early Boeing 737 production aircraft (up to No. 291) used a cold-bonding process for the fuselage skin lap joints. An epoxy-impregnated cloth was used to join the longitudinal edges of the single-thickness 0.036 in (0.91 mm) skin panels together. In addition, the joint was mechanically assembled with three rows of countersunk rivets. Surfaces were cleaned by etching preparatory to bonding. The bond material was kept in a refrigerator until needed and then brought out and allowed to reach room temperature before use. Curing at room temperature took place after assembly. This process was intended to provide structural efficiency and manufacturing cost savings, with weight reduction over fully riveted joints which would have required greater skin thickness for the same fatigue resistance. Specimen tests were made on joint samples, as well as a full-scale test of a fuselage section. This cold-bond lap joint process was discontinued in 1972 and replaced with a different type of sealed lap joint.

Problems encountered with the cold-bond process included difficulty in obtaining thorough cleaning by the etching, condensation on the impregnate during inadequate warm-up to room temperature, or loss of adhesion due to excessive warm-up time causing partial curing before use. If the bond was not secure at manufacture, moisture could enter in service, leading to corrosion and further disbonding, and transfer of load to the rivets. Countersinking of these three rivet rows extended throughout the entire thin skin, so that a knife edge existed at the bottom of the hole which concentrated stresses. These stresses were cyclic with pressurisation loads, and fatigue cracking ultimately occurred at the site.

During the service history of the 737, Boeing issued several service bulletins (SBs) referring to corrosion detection and repair on fuselage skin panels. The earliest was in 1970, others followed in 1972, after the original advice had been moved to the Structural Repair Manual. These bulletins gave advice on the detection and repair of bond failures and corrosion. Operator compliance was not made mandatory by the FAA.

In 1987 the subject SB was elevated to 'alert' status (Rev. 3) because an operator had reported multiple fatigue cracks on three high-cycle (45,000 approx.) aircraft. The FAA issued an airworthiness directive (AD), effective 2 November 1987, which made inspection for fatigue cracking mandatory in certain areas of these early-production aircraft within 250 landings. A further revision of the SB, dated 14 April 1988, permitted an interim repair when cracks were detected and time was not available for complete restoration.

Operator's maintenance history

The aircraft was operated under an FAA-approved continuous airworthiness maintenance programme, based on the manufacturer's maintenance planning document (MPD). This recommends that aircraft inspections and maintenance be divided into four series of checks with specific recurring frequency. The checks are:

A Check. Primary inspection to disclose general condition.
B Check. Intermediate check to determine general condition.
C Check. System and component check, airworthiness evaluation.
D Check. Structural inspection, determine airworthiness.

After Boeing review showed duplication of some C and D items, the MPD was revised and use of the D Check terminology ceased. However, no maintenance items were deleted and many airlines continued with the original terminology. Typical intervals in flight hours are shown in Table 7.1.

Table 7.1 *Maintenance checks carried out on Boeing 737s*

Check	Boeing (1987)	Industry average	Aloha check
A	125	150	175
B	750	650	750
C	3,000	3,000	3,000
D	20,000	20,000	15,000

The Aloha work schedule for checks was prepared initially in 1972. The tasks from the Boeing MPD were organised into 52 increments (blocks) to be accomplished during the D Check interval. The C Check tasks were organised into four increments and integrated with the B Check schedule of work. B, C, and D Checks were actually combined and accomplished in overnight segments. This is typical of short-haul operators with small fleets, who must fly intensively during the day but have spare time for maintenance during the night, and cannot have a single continuous maintenance line as a result.

Aloha Airlines participated in the supplemental structural-inspection programme (SSIP) of FAA advisory circular (AC) 91-56, dated 6 May 1981. The SSIP is a continuous structural inspection to identify cracks, corrosion, and other damage. The SSIP and the supplemental structural inspection document (SSID) provide the operator with procedures to evaluate and supplement their existing programme. The SSID provides for the inspection of significant structural items (SSI) that have damage or fatigue characteristics that could affect the aircraft's structural integrity. Though not related to aircraft fuselage skin in Section 43, the review of the maintenance records found several SSID items for which no maintenance entry could be found.

The airline's aircraft utilisation was such that it took 8 years of flying to reach the 15,000 hr D Check inspection interval. There were 8 blocks of structural inspections in this check, requiring removal of aircraft interior parts. These blocks were to be done sequentially, one at a time, a method agreed by the local FAA principal maintenance inspector (PMI). A single heavy-maintenance hangar visit for a D Check was not scheduled. A complete interior removal at any one time was not required and was not performed. Again, this practice is common for operators of small fleets.

The D Check structural inspection included an FAA-approved one-quarter sampling programme. This meant that certain blocks of the D Check were done on a quarter of the airline's fleet (10 aircraft) at the usual 15,000 hr interval; if no adverse results were found then another quarter of the fleet was inspected at 30,000 hr, and so on. The manufacturer's maintenance planning document (MPD) recommended inspection of all other aircraft in the fleet if there was an adverse finding in the sampling programme, followed by appropriate review and remedial action. The Safety Board saw no adverse findings recorded in its review of the airline's maintenance records.

After the accident, the Safety Board visually inspected the exterior of other aircraft in the airline's fleet and reported considerable evidence of corrosion on the fuselage of the aircraft seen. The Safety Board report also stated that the airline did not produce evidence that it had in place specific severe operating environment corrosion-detection and corrosion-control programmes employing techniques outlined in the aircraft manufacturer's commercial jet corrosion-prevention manual. These requirements included extensive application of water displacing corrosion-inhibiting compounds, re-application at fastener locations and panel edges of exterior fuselage skin every 6 months, and internal treatment at 2-year intervals, washing the aircraft at 15-day intervals, plus regular buffing and brightening of unpainted surfaces. The airline's D Check instructions for structural inspection addressed corrosion with an introductory note. This defined the inspection as a rigorous visual examination for certain conditions, without further definition. Inspectors and quality-control personnel stated that the corrosion was corrected when detected during normal inspection and maintenance activities.

FAA airworthiness directive

AD 87-21-08, issued on 2 November 1987, was issued 'to prevent rapid depressurisation as a result of failure of certain fuselage lap splices . . .'. The AD required operators to perform a 'close visual inspection' of specified areas, and if cracks were found, operators were required to perform an eddy current inspection of the skin around the upper row of lap joint rivets for the full length of the panel. Compliance with the AD was required before the accumulation of 30,000 landings or within 250 landings after the effective date, whichever occurred later. The AD was based on the manufacturer's alert service bulletin (ASB) dated 20 August 1987. The ASB required inspection of the skin around the upper row of rivets at specific fuselage locations. An FAA employee testified that the decision to limit the scope of mandatory inspection was based on analysis of statistical information available and recognition of the extent of work required.

A review of the maintenance discrepancy logs found that two repairs to cracks on a lap joint were made on 12 November 1987. The small separated section of upper fuselage recovered after the accident contained both repairs. The maintenance log for the aircraft indicated that a visual inspection had been made in accordance with AD 87-21-08. However, the record contained no evidence that the required eddy current inspection had been accomplished.

Post-accident investigation

Tests were conducted by airline staff, under Safety Board supervision, on selected portions of the remaining fuselage lap joints to determine the extent of fatigue cracking of the skin along the top row of rivets (the area of highest stress). Initially, the skin around 53 rivets exhibited crack indications, some visually detectable by paint cracks. To make the rivet heads more discernible, the paint was sanded off and the skin reinspected. Twenty-eight of the original 53 indications were confirmed cracks. Sanding off paint in this way is not normal practice. The eddy current inspection along other areas revealed a total of 19 cracks.

Materials laboratory examination

Selected pieces of fuselage skin and associated structure were returned to the Safety Board's Materials Laboratory for analysis. These included that lap joint sample found wedged in the right wing area, and a section of a circumferential butt joint strap. The joint sample contained two external doubler patch repairs. These were removed to examine the holes for evidence of cracks. There was extensive fatigue cracking in the upper-row rivet holes both under and between the patches. The examination found one of the longest cracks on the aircraft, 0.27 in (6.9 mm), in this piece. Also, the entire cold-bonded lap joint had become disbonded. There was light to moderate corrosion with severe corrosion (unrepairable depletion of metal) in some areas. Nearly all of the hot-bonded tear straps were disbonded in the vicinity of the lap joint.

The lap joint samples contained 18 columns of lap joint rivets. The laboratory examination revealed fatigue cracking in the skin adjacent to nearly every hole in the upper rivet row with the larger crack lengths located in the mid-bay areas (half-way between two adjacent circumferential tear straps). Comparison of the final results of the post-accident on-scene eddy current inspections conducted by airline technicians, and of Safety Board laboratory findings, revealed that the on-scene eddy current inspection only successfully identified cracks larger than 0.08 in (2.0 mm). The laboratory examination found five cracks that measured 0.08 in (±0.005). Post-accident inspection had identified only one of the five cracks. The crack-length inspection threshold of 0.08 in varied from the manufacturer's NDT manual which stated, 'This inspection can find cracks 0.040 in or longer beneath the countersunk fastener heads . . .'.

The lap joint piece exhibited fatigue cracking from 16 consecutive rivet holes in the upper row of lap joint rivets. The largest single fatigue crack in one direction measured 0.18 in (4.6 mm) from the knife edge of the countersink. The longest total combined crack length in both directions across a rivet hole measured 0.53 in (13.5 mm). Both the cold-bonded lap joint and hot-bonded tear straps in this area had disbonded. Light to moderate corrosion was present on the previously bonded surfaces.

At the request of the Safety Board, the manufacturer performed a striation count on several of the larger fatigue cracks from the skin along the cabin sides to determine age and crack propagation rate. The results, where possible, are shown in Table 7.2.

Examination of a butt strap section from BS360 revealed circumferentially propagating fatigue cracks from both sides of a rivet hole just forward of the joint line. The fatigue regions extended 0.09 in (2.3 mm) above the rivet hole and 0.03 in (0.76 mm) below the rivet hole.

Safety Board inspection of the three other high-cycle B737s operated by the airline led to two of them being declared beyond economical repair, and the remaining one underwent an extensive refurbishment at an independent aircraft-overhaul facility which kept it out of service for about 1 year.

Table 7.2 Age and crack propagation rate in Aloha Airlines B737

Specimen location	Estimated cycles (±20%)	Crack length in	mm
S-4R	28,670	0.105	2.67
S-4R	37,148	0.130	3.30
S-4R	28,656	0.142	3.61
S-4R	26,449	0.154	3.91
S-4R	24,056	0.110	2.79
S-10L	23,628	0.161	4.09
S-10L	36,379	0.145	3.68

Boeing 737 fail-safe design

Boeing designed the 737 aircraft for an 'economic service life' of 20 years and to include 51,000 flight hours and 75,000 cycles. When the 737 was certified in 1967, the Federal Aviation Regulations (FAR) required that the aircraft's structure be capable of sustaining 80 per cent of limit load with any complete or obvious partial failure of any single structural element. However, the 737 was designed to sustain a full-limit load to account for dynamic effects. The fail-safe design criteria for the 737 established by the manufacturer required that the fuselage be able to withstand a 40 in (1.0 m) crack without suffering catastrophic failure. This was derived from an estimate of the maximum external damage expected to occur to the fuselage from fragments expelled by an uncontained engine failure. There was no consideration given to the joining of adjacent cracks which might develop during extended service other than normal contemporary fatigue evaluation. Boeing design included placing tear straps at 10 in (250 mm) spacing in the fuselage skin in both longitudinal and circumferential directions, to redirect running cracks from external damage in a direction perpendicular to the crack. The fail-safe concept was based on the theory that the redirection of a progressing crack would cause the skin to 'flap' open, releasing internal pressure in a controlled manner without adversely affecting the residual strength of the fuselage.

In the certification programme for the 737, a full-scale fatigue test on a complete fuselage specimen was not done, as it had been for the 727; knowledge gained from the 727 tests was used to validate fatigue performance on the 737. The 737 fatigue tests were made on a representative crown-to-keel half section of the fuselage, which was cycled 150,000 times to full pressure differential (twice the design goal). No fatigue cracks developed in the test section and no disbonding occurred.

Consideration was not given, in the fatigue evaluation, to possible disbonding or corrosion of the fuselage lap joints.

In 1986, Boeing acquired a 737 that had been damaged beyond economical repair in an accident. This was subjected to a thorough teardown and inspection of all structure. In addition, the undamaged rear fuselage was fatigue tested. The specimen had been used for just over 59,000 flight cycles; its lap joints and tear straps were determined to be in good condition. Tests of 70,000 more cycles were applied and some skin cracks found by NDT; further tests up to 89,000 cycles produced cracks ranging up to 0.67 in (17 mm). After this, extra straps were placed on the test piece to preserve it in the event of catastrophic failure, and cycling to 100,673 more resulted in failure from a long crack and flapping skin leading to controlled pressure release.

Supplemental structural inspection programme (SSIP)

With the approach of some high-time aircraft in the world fleet to their original design lives, industry became concerned at the continued airworthiness of the ageing fleet. This led to the development of a continuing structural integrity programme for older transport aircraft. This consisted of directed inspections of structurally significant items (SSIs) at appropriate thresholds and repeated intervals, to detect fatigue damage before the loss of residual strength in the aircraft structure. SSIs are defined as any detail, element or assembly that contributes significantly to carrying flight, ground, pressure or control loads, and whose failure could affect the structural integrity necessary for the safety of the aircraft.

In 1978, part of the airworthiness regulations (14 CFR 25.571) covering fail-safe requirements was revised to reflect advances in fracture mechanics and structural analysis. The new regulation required consideration of damage growth characteristics at multiple sites, and an inspection programme to incorporate these analyses to ensure that the damage was detected before residual strength fell below required fail-safe levels.

Boeing's approach to the ageing fleet problem for the 727/737/747 aircraft types (which were certified under the pre-1978 14 CFR 25.571 codes) was to reassess the aircraft using the revised 14 CFR 25.571 'damage tolerance' requirements. This demanded determination of residual strength in the presence of multiple cracks, extensive analysis of crack growth rates, and incorporation of these results into the aircraft's maintenance programme. Boeing applied the same methods to the reassessment of the early aircraft types as was developed for the newer 757/767 family. The FAA made implementation of the programme mandatory by issuing an airworthiness directive (AD), to be in effect before November 1985 for the 737 aircraft type.

Using a probabilistic approach which assumed that fatigue cracking had occurred in the fleet and that the highest-time aircraft would be most likely to develop cracks first, Boeing recommended a candidate fleet of high-time aircraft for inspection under the SSIP. The B737 candidate fleet comprised about 125 aircraft, including the Aloha Airlines' accident aircraft. Evidence of cracking was to be reported to Boeing for evaluation and potential SB and AD action. Since the programme was intended to detect previously unknown fatigue cracking, the SSI was to be dropped from the programme once fatigue cracking became known and corrected through the AD process.

A structural classification system was developed to determine which SSIs would be included in the SSIP. The principle was to include only those SSIs for which damage detection had to be done by planned inspection. SSIs were excluded if damage was obvious or a malfunction evident, examples being wing skin evidenced by fuel leaks or fuselage skin revealed by controlled decompression through flapping. Other manufacturers included fuselage skin in their requirements.

Aloha airlines had incorporated the SSIP into its maintenance programme for the candidate aircraft. The FAA approved the airline's supplementary structural inspection document (SSID) programme into its maintenance schedule. According to the Safety Board report, no items were discovered or reported by the airline following the SSID inspections.

Surveillance and monitoring of the operator

FAA surveillance of Aloha Airlines maintenance was the responsibility of a principal maintenance inspector (PMI), whose duties included guidance in the development of maintenance documentation, review of inspection time limits, overseeing training programmes, and monitoring of maintenance programmes. The PMI was responsible for nine carriers and seven repair stations located across a wide area, and stated that travel distances reduced the time available for surveillance of each operator. The PMI was assigned in January 1987, and stated that he was neither made aware of the high-time status of some Aloha aircraft, nor did he receive any information regarding the in-service testing of the B737 done by the manufacturer in late 1987.

A Boeing survey team visited the airline as part of the ageing fleet programme required by the SSID, the first visit being in September 1987. A meeting to discuss the findings took place on 28 October 1987, at which Boeing personnel voiced concern about corrosion and skin patches found on the two aircraft and made recommendations. A survey of another Aloha aircraft, as part of the ageing fleet programme, was made in January 1988.

A Boeing team also visited Aloha's facility in November 1987 in response to a request for upgrading and modernisation of their maintenance programme. The report on this was delivered on 30 January 1988 and made 37 recommendations; a meeting to discuss these was held on 14 April 1988. The recommendations detailed inspection and repair work on a number of aircraft.

National aviation safety inspection programme (NASIP)

This programme of in-depth inspections exists to determine compliance with FARs, including FAA-approved policies. A special FAA inspection of the airline, as part of this programme, was made in December 1987. The report on this contained numerous compliance findings, and criticised the airline's maintenance management in respect of training procedures and repair classification, among other things.

FAA action following the accident

The day after the accident, the FAA issued an AD applicable to all Boeing 737s over 55,000 landings, requiring flight at reduced cabin pressure and inspection of certain lap joints and circumferential splices. This AD was superseded by another AD, of 4 May 1988, applicable to all B737s over 30,000 landings, requiring inspections of specific lap joints implicated in the original accident, with reporting of findings. Replies from 18 operators showed 49 cases of corrosion or minor cracking. Multiple-site cracking existed in 14 aircraft. A post-accident evaluation of the airline was made in May 1988 by a special FAA team. Further ADs were issued in November 1988 and December 1988, requiring inspections of splices and bonding. A Notice of Proposed Rulemaking (NPRM), dated October 1988, made replacement of the upper rivet rows in the lap splices mandatory. The final rule was published as AD 89-09-03, effective 8 May 1989.

A 'Conference On Older Airplanes' was organised by the FAA in June 1988, and resulted in the formation of an industry task force, led by the Air Transport Association (ATA), which recommended a modification or replacement programme to assure airworthiness of older aircraft. This task force involved representatives from manufacturers, operators and authorities in all major air transport nations. As a result, early-model Boeing 727, 737 and 747 aircraft receive extra maintenance and inspection requiring modification or replacement of parts, rather than continued inspection. Areas affected include lap and bonded joints which show delamination or corrosion. Many other changes are being made. The FAA has issued a NPRM for each aircraft type, proposing the mandatory completion of modifications listed in Boeing documents when an aircraft reaches its economic design life, or within four years, whichever is later. Other manufacturers' older-model aircraft are under review for similar proposals.

In addition, the FAA Flight Standards Service has created an ageing fleet programme, forming evaluation teams to visit airlines and evaluate corrosion control programmes, structural inspection techniques and AD accomplishment. The objective is to allow ageing aircraft to continue safely in revenue service.

Effectiveness of inspections

Examination of recovered parts of the accident aircraft's structure led the Safety Board to conclude that, at the time of the AD inspection in November 1987, the cracks in one specimen must have ranged from about 0.09 in to 0.13 in (2.3 mm to 3.3 mm). Eddy current inspections performed after the accident could not detect cracks under 0.08 in (2.0 mm), but the inspection reliably detected cracks larger than 0.08 in (2.0 mm). Since the post-accident analysis indicated that cracks existed in the structure above this length, and were well within the detectable size for eddy current inspection, such cracks should have been detected along the upper row of rivets in the cabin wall lap joint. This suggests inadequacy of inspection procedures.

There are several possible reasons why inspectors might fail to find the detectable crack in the lap joint. First, the human element associated with visual inspection. Anyone can perform a critical task once to a satisfactory level, but repetitive operation brings factors such as expectation of results, boredom, task length, isolation during the task, and environmental conditions, which all tend to inhibit performance.

Another factor affecting people involved in maintenance and inspection is the effect of biological — or circadian — rhythms. Airline maintenance is often done at night or in the early morning, times which are known to cause adverse human performance. Maintenance programmes should take account of this and of the possible effects of sleep loss and irregular shift patterns, when task scheduling.

For example, compliance with the AD required a close visual inspection of the lap joints, and eddy current inspection of the upper row of lap joint rivets along the entire panel; 1,300 rivets needed close visual inspection and about 360 rivets per panel might need eddy current inspection. Inspection of these required a climb onto scaffolding and working along the upper fuselage carrying a light; the eddy current inspection required a probe, meter, and light. Occasionally the inspector had to use ropes hanging from the rafters to avoid falling off the aircraft whilst inspecting rivet rows. Inspection of skin areas around many rivets for signs of very small cracks, in such a physically uncomfortable environment, is tedious. If many areas are found to have no cracks, the expectation that there are no cracks at all becomes stronger. Testimony to this effect was given by an industrial engineering specialist.

Another factor that may have affected the performance of the airline's maintenance and inspection personnel was related to the quality of support provided by management to assist these persons in the performance of their tasks. Proper training, guidance and procedures are needed, as well as an adequate working environment, sufficient time, and an understanding of the importance of their duties, to ensure the airworthiness of the aircraft. The airline's training records revealed that little formal training was provided in nondestructive inspection (NDI) techniques. Also, the airline's full utilisation of aircraft during the daytime resulted in most maintenance being done at night. The risk is that such patterns tend to drive for the completion of required maintenance, forcing workers to perform under time pressure.

The Safety Board also gave the opinion that the inspection tasks of airline maintenance personnel were exacerbated by the fact that FAA-approved training for aircraft maintenance technicians contained material largely irrelevant to the tasks actually performed by licensed personnel in an airline environment; new technology such as fly-by-wire and composites did not appear in the list of required curriculum subjects. Existing requirements for training aviation maintenance personnel failed to address the tasks that such personnel actually did. The Safety Board report asked the FAA to examine the regulations governing certification of aviation maintenance technician schools and the licensing of mechanics, and to revise the regulations to address contemporary developments in aircraft maintenance.

Another area where concern was expressed was the absence of FAA requirements for formal training or licensing of NDI personnel. The Board noted that the UK CAA and those in other countries had formally recognised the importance of NDI skills, and required in-depth training, skill demonstration, licensing and recurrent certification of NDI personnel. NDI technology and techniques in some US industries had advanced, with certification to American Society for Nondestructive Testing (ASNT) guidelines, but the US aviation industry had not applied such advanced practices. The Safety Board recommended that the FAA review the NDI maintenance function with a view toward formal training, skill demonstration, apprenticeships, formal licensing and certification.

Selection of inspection personnel was another issue raised in the investigation. Appointment by seniority to a task of repetitive and tedious nature implied by NDI might be inappropriate; persons who have demonstrated a capability for supervisory duties might not perform well at these tasks. The FAA was recommended to include selection of inspectors in its human factors research programme.

The Safety Board was concerned that NDI methods in the aviation industry were heavily dependent on human performance of repetitive and detailed tasks. Use of automation or other techniques should be developed to minimise potential errors inherent in human action of such tasks.

THE LUSAKA INCIDENT

Summary

On 14 May 1977 a Boeing 707-321C of Dan-Air Services Ltd, flying a cargo service from London to Zambia, was approaching Lusaka Airport at about 2 miles (4 km) from the runway threshold when the right tailplane detached from the airframe. The aircraft pitched nose down and dived vertically into open ground from an altitude of about 800 ft (250 m) and caught fire. There were no survivors from the six crew members.

The cause of the accident was found to be a combination of fatigue failure and inadequate fail-safe design in the right tailplane spar. Shortcomings in design assessment, certification and inspection were contributory factors.

Aircraft design

In the original Boeing 707-100 series design of the 1950s, the tailplane spanwise rear spar was of the conventional design with two booms (or 'chords'), upper and lower, joined by a thin skin shear web. Fail-safe design of these was demonstrated for certification purposes by dynamically failing a special top chord attachment pin during a ground test programme, so allowing the front spar structure to carry the bending loads and transfer them to the centre section. The manufacturers also carried out a tailplane fatigue test to investigate the sensitivity of the structure to fatigue damage. During fatigue testing of the 100 series tailplanes, a fatigue crack was produced in the rear spar top chord, but this was not related to the crack found in the Lusaka accident.

When the Boeing 707-300 series aircraft was developed by lengthening the 100 series fuselage dimensions, the tailplane was redesigned. Span was increased to provide more pitching movement, and to cater for the resulting higher load, the fail-safe capability of the structure was improved by the provision of a third spanwise chord and root fitting located at mid-spar depth on the rear spar centreline. This design, in effect, provided a redundant spar boom, so that failure of any one boom would not be catastrophic. No fatigue tests were carried out on the redesigned tailplane structure.

During the 300 series test flying programme the aircraft was found to have unsatisfactory elevator-response characteristics. The cause of this was identified as inadequate tailplane torsional stiffness, so that elevator movement in one direction caused tailplane twist in the opposite sense and reduced the control effect required. The torsional rigidity of the tailplane structure was restored by doubling the tailplane's light alloy lower skin over the inboard region of the torsion box and by changing the material of the corresponding top skin to stainless steel, with a suitable adjustment of skin thickness.

Both UK BCAR and US CAR, at the time of design, contained safe fatigue life or fail-safe design options. The Boeing 707 was designed to comply with the requirements of the fail-safe option. Neither the US nor the British airworthiness regulations specifically required fatigue testing. In both cases the manufacturer was permitted to demonstrate compliance 'by analysis and/or tests'. Also, for the safe fatigue life case, it was acceptable that the service history of aircraft of similar design, taking into account differences in operating conditions and procedures, be used as a basis for fatigue life assessment.

For the Boeing 707-400 series aircraft, which was essentially a 300 series with Rolls-Royce engines, in relation to fatigue integrity of the structure a British type certificate was awarded on the basis of a US FAA certificate of compliance with the fail-safe option of the relevant CAR together with an ARB specified special condition. This condition required that a cracked structure should withstand limit flight loads, generally somewhat higher than loads specified in the CAR, and the submission of an inspection programme designed to detect cracks before they reached dangerous proportions. The 400 series was actually accepted onto the British register before the 321C series, since the latter was an all-cargo derivative of an existing passenger design (passenger windows and furnishings being deleted in favour of floor strengthening and pallet handling gear, among other alterations).

Structural testing of the 300 series design beyond that done on the 100 series design was not performed because US airworthiness requirements did not specify it. The airworthiness criteria were met by calculations which were deemed to show that the static and fail-safe strengths of the 300 series tailplane were adequate for the designed purpose. UK regulations for tailplanes required that 'parts which may be critical from fatigue aspects shall be subjected to such analysis and load tests as to demonstrate either a safe fatigue life or that such parts of the primary structure exhibited the characteristics of a failsafe structure'. No such tests were called for by the UK ARB, who based their acceptance of the aircraft type on the US certification which had taken into account the 707-100 series tests together with analysis of the 707-300 series design.

Maintenance schedules

For operation on the British register a maintenance schedule approved by the UK CAA is required. The manufacturers publish a 'Maintenance and Planning Data' document (BMPD) for the 707 series aircraft, intended to give guidance for operators and their respective airworthiness authorities in drawing up each individual operator's maintenance schedule. In practice the BMPD usually forms the basis of the initial 'approved maintenance schedule', but it should be emphasised that the information it contains is for guidance only. The document is divided into volumes, with the first volume covering the normal maintenance A, B and C type checks, and the second volume covering the structural inspections designed to highlight critical areas in the structure.

Regular inspection items in the BMPD which cover the tailplane rear spar outboard were listed under C Check items and called for visual inspection (to a standard defined in the document) of the tailplane 'exterior surfaces' and the 'rear spar and hinge fittings'. The C Check inspection did not require access panels to be opened. The opening of access panels was a requirement in the inspection called up in volume II, which required a more searching inspection of the rear spar structure. This required that the rear spar structure be inspected internally through access panels in the trailing edge structure and via the leading edge panels. The operator is advised to 'inspect spar and rib chords, webs and stiffeners for cracks or loose fasteners'. The recommended period for this inspection was continually being modified in the light of service experience, but at the time of the accident was for a quarter of the fleet to be inspected every 21,000 flying hours.

The UK CAA-approved operator's maintenance schedule applicable to the aircraft was generally similar to the recommendation given in the BMPD. However, there were significant detail changes. The 'exterior surfaces' check listed in the BMPD appeared as 'external skin — CHK' (with a CAA-defined meaning of 'CHK', i.e. check, listed in the front of the schedule). In addition to the instruction to 'CHK' there was the note '— close visual inspection check all exterior plates closed'. In the case of the BMPD's entry 'Rear spar and hinge fittings', there was no corresponding direct reference to the rear spar contained in the operator's schedule, although the 'hinge fittings' were covered as a part of the elevator checks. The corresponding work card used by the operator contained no direct reference to the rear spar. It did however give the instruction to inspect, among other items, 'all visible structure' which, if carried out, would cover the rear spar to the same level as the exterior surfaces entry in the BMPD. It also listed five key points, which covered cracks in the structure parts. The BMPD's structural inspection was reproduced without alteration in the operator's schedule, but the period between inspections was reduced to a quarter fleet every 14,000 flying hours.

Design considerations

The design and subsequent stiffening of the 300 series tailplane was accompanied by re-stressing limited to ensuring that the static strength was not reduced by the modification, which was made after the basic stress analysis work had been done. It was known that the greater stiffness of the stainless steel skin would result in higher skin loadings, and hence higher loads in the steel fasteners towards the root end of the rear spar top chord. These higher fastener loads would also increase the bearing stress in the top chord forward flange. However, given the existing chord flange design, little could be done to improve this situation because the use of larger-diameter fasteners to reduce bearing stresses would have reduced the edge margin to an unacceptable level. However, it was considered that the design was adequate in this area, given the general acceptance at that time of its fail-safe capability. It was not realised that the skin modification, whilst improving the static strength, would significantly reduce the fatigue strength. This was the first of a chain of events which culminated in the accident.

Fail-safe design philosophy

A fail-safe design is one in which there are one or more redundant structural elements which are capable, in the event of a failure of one or more primary load members, of carrying the flight loads. However, a fail-safe design is only so while the degree of redundancy is sufficient to cater for a failure; in other words, a singly redundant structure (as in this case) is only fail-safe while the primary structure is intact. Once this has failed, the principle of safe-life obtains, and it becomes necessary to find the failure in the primary structure before the fail-safe members themselves can become weakened by fatigue, corrosion or any other mechanism. Because the strength reserves in the fail-safe mode are usually well below those of the intact structure, this means that in practice the failure must be found and appropriate action taken within a short time compared with the normal life of the structure. Obviously the degree of urgency which attaches to a given failure depends on the design of that particular structure and its stress and corrosion environment, as well as the type of operations being flown. But it remains a fact that, in order to maintain the safety of a fail-safe structure, there must be an inspection programme forming an integral part of the total design, to ensure that a failure in any part of the primary structure is identified well before any erosion of the strength of the redundant fail-safe structure can occur.

The concept of fail-safe structures (as understood in 1978) depends on the following inter-related factors, all necessary for safe implementation of the philosophy:

(a) Adequate design to cater for the basic operating and load environment in a manner which:
— meets the basic structural strength requirements for the intact structure;
— predicts and minimises the likelihood of significant damage or failure in the primary structure caused by fatigue, corrosion, accidental damage, or for any other reason;
— provides adequate access to (and identification of) primary structure so that regular inspection for failure or damage can be accomplished easily;
— can, in the event of a failure of any part of the primary structure, sustain the flight loads with adequate safety margins for a period long enough to enable the failure to be detected during routine inspection;
— utilises suitable materials for each element in the design;

— defines those areas of structure which fall into the category of primary structure, and gives adequate guidance as to the type of inspection which should be carried out and the maximum periods between such inspections.

(b) Quality control — to ensure that each aircraft is built and serviced with spares which meet the design specification.

(c) Adequate maintenance — the implementation of a suitable maintenance schedule which incorporates in a suitable form the 'fail-safe design' inspection package produced by the manufacturer.

(d) Feedback, to the manufacturer and airworthiness authorities, of information about significant failures and recurring failures — so that any shortcomings in the design can be detected and remedial action can be taken.

In the case of the Boeing 707-300 series tailplane at this time, only the basic structural strength requirements of the intact structure and the quality-control requirements appear to have been completely satisfied.

Tailplane failure

The complete failure of this structure was the result of two factors. First, the failure through fatigue damage of the rear spar top chord; second, the inability of the redundant fail-safe structure to carry flight loads for a long enough period to enable detection of the fatigue crack by normal inspection procedures.

Detailed examination revealed that the fatigue failure of the top chord originated in the upper edge of a skin fastener hole, and that the crack had been growing over a period of some 7,200 flights before chord failure occurred. The reason why a crack should develop at that location was not immediately obvious. The design of the tailplane torsion box and skin structure meant that bending stresses in the skin could not be resisted by the inner closure rib, so these stresses would be taken by the spar chords near this rib and thus produce higher fastener loads there than further out in the tailplane. The use of a stainless steel skin would also increase load transfer into the spar chord because of its greater stiffness. The manufacturer anticipated higher fastener loads in this area, and recommended hi-shear fasteners, having steel inserts rather than light alloy as used further outboard. However, some of these fasteners had been replaced with lower-strength ones at some time in the previous maintenance, for unknown reasons.

Examination of top skin fastener holes in the unbroken left tailplane showed similar hole distortions to those in the right side. It appeared that the crack occurred at the 11th fastener because loads further inboard were high enough to distort the fastener and skin, and so relieve the load. More tests indicated that stresses in this area might be higher than anticipated by the designers.

Failure of the fail-safe structure

The design was certificated as fail-safe, on the basis that failure of a single principal structural element would probably not lead to catastrophic failure. The fail-safe component in the rear spar consisted of an additional spar chord and root fitting located at mid-spar depth. In normal service this chord was not loaded. Calculations indicated that this design should have been able to tolerate normal loads in flight. The accident revealed that this fail-safe behaviour did not happen. Tests on another tailplane, cut to represent the fatigue failure prior to the accident, produced a failing load similar in magnitude to that estimated by calculation of the maximum load likely to be experienced on airfield approach. Strain analysis of this test piece showed the stress distribution to be different from that assumed by the designers in the event of top chord failure. Load was transferred round the fracture and back into the top, which caused the centre chord to fail as a result of stress concentration.

Maintenance practice

The BMPD recommendations specify the areas of structure and types of inspection for the regular checks. The terms used are defined. For the tailplane, only two entries cover the rear spar top chord; both using the word 'check', previously defined as a thorough examination of an item for general condition with special emphasis in a large number of areas. A time allocation was given which tended to suggest that an external visual inspection was intended rather than, for example, a more detailed eddy-current check. Discussion with the manufacturer revealed some ambiguity in the wording about exactly which parts were to be inspected, but it was concluded that the recommended inspection should have been adequate to detect a crack in the top chord, provided the crack was reasonably visible.

It was known from other experience that partial cracks visible to the naked eye, once located, are for practical purposes undetectable visually, even with the aid of a dye penetrant. Thus the recommended inspection could not have been expected to detect the crack in the top spar chord unless the C Check occurred during the interval between top chord severance and total spar failure, which did not happen in this case. The need to detect the crack during its early stages was a consequence of the shortcomings in the fail-safe design, of which there was no knowledge before the accident. If the structure had behaved as expected, the reserve strength would have allowed a crack to open up sufficiently for detection at the next C Check.

The airline's inspection schedule was also commented on by the investigators, with reference to the wording of tasks. It was concluded that the schedule, and to a large extent those of other UK operators, placed insufficient emphasis on the rear spar structure and the top chord in particular. These shortcomings were not considered directly relevant to the accident because the inspection recommendations were based on the design fail-safe assumptions and because of the lack of sufficient access to the forward face of the spar.

THE BOEING 747 CARGO DOOR LOSS

Summary

On 24 February 1989, a United Airlines (UAL) Boeing 747 aircraft lost a cargo-hold door while in flight near Hawaii. The aircraft suffered an explosive decompression and damage to two of the engines. Cabin structure in the region of the door frame was torn away, and nine passengers were swept overboard and killed. The crew made a successful emergency descent to land back at Honolulu airport. Damage to the aircraft alone cost $14 million.

The safety investigators concluded that the probable cause was a damaged door-locking mechanism, and determined that the airline, the FAA and the Boeing Company contributed to the accident.

The NSTB report said that Boeing and the FAA knew the cargo door locking mechanism was flawed nearly two years before the accident. The board cited a 1987 Pan American Boeing 747 incident in which the door opened in flight.

Malfunctions of the door in the UAL 747, with either electrical or manual operations, damaged eight lock sectors, which help to keep the latches in place against pressurisation load, according to the Board.

The Safety Board concluded that corrective action should have been taken more quickly by Boeing and the FAA, and that the airline's maintenance department should have noted the recurring problems with the cargo door. The accident was preceded by defect log entries, according to the Director, Major Investigations Division, of the NTSB's Office of Aviation Safety.

The Safety Board recommended that the FAA require installation of warning lights, for cockpit crew and ground personnel, that independently confirm whether the door is locked. Boeing said the Safety Board judgement was premature without examination of the cargo door, which was located at a depth of 17,000 ft (5,200 m) in the ocean. Board officials said that findings would be reviewed if recovery of the door was possible and analysis showed any new information.

A Boeing official said all Boeing 747 operators have incorporated terminating actions that have made the operation of the door safe. A terminating action is a hardware repair that eliminates the need for inspections. In answer to Board criticism, Boeing says it responded quickly to the PanAm incident on 10 March 1987. This aircraft developed pressurisation problems during a flight scheduled from London to New York, and returned to London where the cargo door was found to be partly open along the lower edge. Investigation showed a master latch-lock handle was closed, turning off the cockpit warning light for the cargo door. It was concluded that a ground-service employee had back-driven the latches manually at the bottom of the door after it was closed and the master-lock latch-lock handle shut. Boeing issued an alert service bulletin (ASB) within days of the 1987 incident. Boeing and the FAA agreed on a terminating action, issued 5 months after the incident. This required riveting a doubler to locking sectors for extra strength and capability to prevent rotation of the latch cams in the event of improper back-driving attempts.

The FAA issued an airworthiness directive (AD) requiring tasks described by Boeing in May 1988, for completion by November 1989. The UAL aircraft was therefore in compliance. However, a transcription error in the advance copy of the FAA AD eliminated some words and altered the meaning of inspections required.

The UAL door was damaged by intermittent malfunctions before the accident, according to the Safety Board report. The door was incorrectly rigged, and the latch cams and locking sectors began to wear. According to the NTSB director, maintenance staff inspected the door at night when the aircraft was empty, so that problems encountered under loading were not revealed. The investigator said that fuselage flexing can occur with the heavy strains of a maximum gross weight take-off. He emphasised the need for careful inspection of cargo doors. Problems with the electrical operation of the door had led to airline workers using manual operation three months before the incident. A directive in effect at the time of the accident required visual examination of the door and locking mechanism if the door had been operated manually.

The investigator said that the 1987 incident proved that the door could appear to be locked whilst it was not. Therefore the locking mechanism did not provide for the intended fail-safe provisions of locking and cockpit indications.

THE MANCHESTER INCIDENT

Summary

During take-off from Manchester airport on 22 August 1985, a Boeing 737-200 operated by British Airtours experienced an engine failure caused by a burst combustion can. Fragments from the explosion pierced the wing fuel tank at the access panel provided for refuelling. A large fire developed quickly; cockpit instruments and airport ATC gave warning of this, but the severity was not apparent while the aircraft continued in motion. When the aircraft came to rest, the flames soon penetrated the cabin, causing the interior to burn. Evacuation could not be made in time to avoid the deaths of 55 of the 137 passengers and crew.

The UK Department of Transport Air Accident Investigation Branch (AAIB) investigation report concluded that the cause of the accident was an uncontained failure of the left engine, initiated by a failure of the No. 9 combustion can, which had been repaired. Part of the can, expelled from the engine, struck and fractured the underwing fuel tank access panel. Fire developed and the effects were increased by the rest position of the aircraft in relation to the wind, even though this was light.

Contributory factors were the vulnerability of the fuel tank access panels to impact damage, lack of effective provision for fighting major fires inside the cabin, the vulnerability of the aircraft hull to external fire, and the highly toxic emissions of burning aircraft-interior furnishings.

The major cause of fatalities was rapid incapacitation due to inhaling smoke and gases inside the burning cabin. Delays in evacuation caused by difficulty in opening a door aggravated this.

Damage to the aircraft

The left engine combustion casing was split open, causing substantial secondary damage to the engine and its housing. The forward section of the No. 9 combustion can was ejected through the damaged engine casing. A fuel tank access panel on the lower surface of the wing just outboard of the engine was punctured, making a large hole in the base of the main fuel tank which is integral with the wing structure. Fire and explosions had damaged the left wing.

Parts of the rear fuselage left sidewall and most of the cabin roof were burnt away, and the rear fuselage with the tail section had fallen to the ground. Most of the cabin interior was extensively burnt and the floor in the rear of the passenger cabin had collapsed down into the rear cargo hold. Unburnt areas of the cabin interior were covered in soot.

The accident and subsequent report highlighted many known problems about fire safety in aircraft. This eventually led to changes to UK airworthiness regulations and modifications to aircraft aimed at increasing the survival of passengers by delaying combustion of furnishing materials — the 'fire-blocking' layers required in seat construction being one example. Other proposals made, or still being studied, include wider emergency evacuation doors, onboard fire suppression equipment, passenger smoke hoods, and external television cameras on the aircraft. There had been other aircraft accidents in which fire occurred, and methods for dealing with this were under discussion by authorities and manufacturers, but international negotiations take a long time to reach agreement. The AAIB report describes the fire and its consequences. This account is concerned with the engine and its maintenance, since this is of more relevance here.

Engine features

The engine was a Pratt & Whitney JT8D-15 two-shaft turbofan. The combustion chamber design is described as 'can-annular', consisting of 9 combustion cans enclosed in a combustion-chamber outer case. Each can contains a fuel burner and combustion takes place inside the can, which is cooled by air flow, to resist the very high temperatures. The cooling depends on a carefully designed system of air passages; damage to these by deformation leads to rapid failure because the flame temperature exceeds the melting point of the metal. The chamber outer case has to withstand the compressor delivery pressure, of about 16 atmospheres at take-off.

The combustion cans are made from a front dome of Stellite® alloy followed by a series of 11 liners in Hastelloy® X sheet. The dome has swirl vanes to direct the incoming air for mixing with the burner. The liners are ring-shaped and vary in diameter to provide the required cross-section. Joining is by resistance seam-welding at manufacture. Cans are mounted so that thermal expansion is possible without affecting the location necessary for even combustion.

Combustion cans in this particular engine were to the latest modification standard, devised to counter cracking of the seam weld between liners 2 and 3 observed in previous versions.

Engines in the accident aircraft

The left engine was about five years old at the time of the accident, initially fitted to a different aircraft. After about three years' use, it was removed and stripped for inspection. A task known as light maintenance inspection (LMI) was performed and it was then rebuilt with repaired combustion cans from another engine. This had run for 7482 hours with 3371 cycles of use, and was removed following reports of high exhaust-gas temperature and signs of compressor damage. The repairs were made to cracked areas in the 3rd liners. The engine strip report had noted burning and cracking to five of the combustion cans. Radiographic inspection of the liner area was done, and the plates retained; the accident investigators were able to examine these plates, which also covered areas up to liner 5. Cracks were evident in several cans, with can No. 9 being the most affected in the 3/4 liner joint area.

All of these cracks were treated by a direct-fusion weld process during the LMI routine. Pre-weld solution heat treatment and post-weld stress relief were not done, for reasons explained later. The repaired cans were then fitted to an engine which became the left engine of the accident aircraft, running a further 4,611 flying hours and 2,036 flight cycles before the accident. At the accident the cans had run for 12,093 hours and 5,397 cycles since new; the engine had run 14,503 hours and 6,552 cycles.

Engine history

Examination of the aircraft technical log records showed a number of flight-crew entries concerning slow acceleration from start, slow start, and mismatch of throttle position between the two engines when set at the same nominal power by instrument readings. The left engine appeared to require a more advanced throttle position than the right, for the same power. Maintenance action was usually directed to the engine control system; this appeared to cure the symptoms, therefore internal examination of the engine was not done.

In August 1985, log reports of slow acceleration for the left engine appeared. Maintenance action was taken on the engine control and fuel system, but slow acceleration was again reported. Finally, an acceptable deferred defect (ADD) was raised on 21 August for a full trim run, after further inspection and maintenance of the engine control system. The aircraft made two more flights on this day, the last before the accident, with no further flight crew comment about the engines. Interview with maintenance technicians involved in the work of 21 August established that signs of throttle mismatch still persisted after adjustments had been made to the engine controls. The full trim run specified in the ADD was to be done at the operator's London Gatwick main base, where the necessary test equipment was held.

Engine examination

After removal from the aircraft, the left engine was given a detailed strip and examination in an overhaul workshop. Apart from the combustion section damage it appeared to be in good condition. Damage in other areas was probably due to the effects of the combustion-chamber case rupture. All parts of the combustion section were thoroughly examined at the manufacturer's premises and at RAE Farnborough under AAIB supervision.

Only the front dome of the No. 9 combustion can could be extensively examined for cracks, because the rearward Nos 3 and 4 liners had mostly burnt away or been discharged by the explosion. Evidence of fatigue fracture was apparent, originating in many places and so causing simultaneous growth of cracks. As noted before, previous cracks had been identified during workshop inspection and repaired, but cracks re-formed in similar positions after this, and were joined by another major crack. Microscopic examination revealed that these major cracks were composed of many smaller ones growing from separate origins. Patches of fatigue growth linking the major cracks were found, this fatigue damage was different from that seen in the other microscopic crack areas. Cracks did not always re-form in the welded repairs, sometimes a new crack appeared beside the weld.

The weld repair was checked by microscopic examination. Voids, cracks and inclusions were detected in the weld repairs, but this was not regarded as significant because of the evidence that new cracks did not follow the path of the original. Investigators believed that other factors, such as material thickness build-up after the welding, and local temperature distribution in service, would be just as important.

The combustion-chamber outer case was examined to establish the reason for rupture. Measurements showed that a 175 mm length near the No. 9 can had suffered reduced thickness and finally bulged outwards. Data on previous chamber-case failures, provided by the engine manufacturer, suggested that a crack length exceeding 117 mm would be likely to cause explosive rupture. Case overheating would therefore not result in an explosion if it occurred over a smaller area, in which case burning through would be likely. The engine fire warning system would give adequate notice of this failure.

The fuel nozzles from the engine were tested to see if their condition might be responsible for uneven combustion; no evidence of this was found. The fuel control unit (FCU) was also examined and tested to see if its behaviour had any bearing on the accident. No evidence of inability to maintain a repeatable idle speed setting was found; the idle trim screw was found to be in mid-range position. The unit was in a condition expected after 15,000 hours of service, and was concluded to be capable of running the engine throughout its normal speed and power range.

Tests

A series of special tests was made on an engine fitted with different cans, which had been coated in thermal-sensitive paint. This paint changes to different colours according to temperature ranges experienced, and is commonly used in combustion chamber development by manufacturers. The engine was run through a typical departure and take-off sequence, idled for a short time and then shut down. The cans were removed for examination, and a suitable can was then instrumented with thermocouples and further tested. Tests were conducted to simulate the operator's routes, rather than the extremes expected for the engine.

Results indicated similar temperature distributions in all nine cans, with hot spots in the region 825−950°C for the third liners of eight cans, and two cans with hot spots over 1025°C. Maximum material temperature occurred at highest power, not at any other transient condition. Hot-spot temperature rose rapidly as peak power was approached. These results were used to estimate thermal stress levels, temperature gradients of 150−200°C over 2−3 mm being shown in the tests. Stress levels of 29,000 psi (200 MPa) were predicted, tests on the can material gave a fatigue life of between 100 cycles at 980°C and 1,000,000 cycles at 815°C at this stress. This illustrates the dangerous consequences of uneven temperatures and local hot spots in this critical area.

Experience of other operators

The Pratt & Whitney JT8D Series is the most widely used type in the world, with many versions since its first use in 1964. The JT8D-15 engine used in this Boeing 737-200 series aircraft has the highest combustion can temperatures of any model in the range.

There had been twelve reported incidents of combustion-chamber outer case rupture before this accident, seven of these were attributed to a primary defect in the case, two to fuel nozzle and/or support problems, the remaining three to combustion can problems. In at least two events, parts of the can had been discharged by explosion causing airframe damage but no fire. Other incidents of burn-through in the outer case were also considered relevant; there were sixteen of these recorded, four attributed to can failure, five to can shifting, and the rest to fuel problems.

The three incidents of explosive rupture in the outer case were in 1979, 1984 and 1985. After the 1979 event, the engine manufacturer sent a letter to all operators describing the incident and advising operators to inspect for cracking in specific liner seam welds and recommending a repair scheme. It also stated 'liner separation in some cases, is evidenced by slow spool-up from light off to idle or by slow acceleration above idle'. The letter described a development programme to understand the cracking and improve repair and management procedures. This was expected to finish in July 1980. Meanwhile, operators were recommended to use solution heat treatment prior to weld repair, as specified in the approved engine manual. A further letter was sent on 5 December 1980, stating that circumferential cracking was caused by thermal fatigue and that complete 360° cracking generally occurred in weld-repaired liners, having lower fatigue strength than non-weld repaired liners. More recommendations were made for inspection and repair. Another letter, on 13 May 1983, went primarily to overhaul agencies and introduced a braze reinforcement repair, claimed to improve fatigue life in can seam-welds. This process was withdrawn a few months after the Manchester accident.

Lastly, a message sent by wire to all operators on 7 February 1985 cited two recent incidents of outer case failure, and again warned that reports of slow starting or slow acceleration should be suspected as signs of combustion damage.

At the Engine Operators Conferences in 1980 and 1985, the manufacturer referred to can cracking problems and repeated the content of the letters issued in those years. The 1985 Conference also described cracking in the seam weld location and said that 'most reports of problems concerned high time parts which had been weld repaired many times'.

A service bulletin issued in November 1980 by the engine manufacturer introduced a redesigned combustion can, incorporating improvements in the liner seam welding and better wear resistance to mounting faces. It was primarily aimed at curing seam-weld cracking of the 2/3 liner joint, which occurs under an air-scoop and therefore requires radiographic inspection. All engines delivered to the operator had this modification.

A further service bulletin, issued in April 1983 for JT8D-15 engines fitted with this modified combustion, introduced a modification with ceramic coating of the interior to increase thermal insulation. Background information in the bulletin noted that burning and cracking had been observed in some combustion cans after only 3,000 to 5,000 hours of operation. This modification was not mandatory, and was not incorporated by the manufacturer in new cans; only a few operators appear to have fitted it.

Engine maintenance

The engine manufacturer does not specify a fixed time for strip inspection and overhaul of the whole engine. Some parts of the engine are hard-lifed, which may provide an opportunity for strip. The details of a maintenance schedule are a matter for the operator and Airworthiness Authority involved. A 'Maintenance Planning Guidelines' booklet produced by the engine manufacturer gives assistance in selecting the appropriate maintenance process, from hard-time, modular overhaul, condition monitoring and on-condition maintenance, with suggested initial inspection intervals.

After negotiations with the CAA, the operator proceeded with an engine sampling programme in which engines were removed and strip-inspected at intervals to monitor deterioration; this was intended to establish overhaul lives for the major engine parts. Sample inspection would begin at 5,000 hours since new, after which each engine would run for 10,000 to 12,000 hours since new, before the LMI action; this would include a combustion section overhaul. Heavy maintenance inspection (HMI) would be done at 16,000 hours since last HMI or since new. The LMI would be repeated at 10,000 hour intervals. It is apparent from these rules that the engine of the accident aircraft would have been due for a second overhaul at 16,000 hours.

The manufacturer's maintenance-planning guidelines document was also used to produce the operator's approved maintenance schedule (AMS) for the engine type. The guidelines recommended visual and X-ray inspection of the combustion chambers, apparently with no particular area for the X-ray. The AMS specified the No. 3 liner seam-weld for X-ray because an air-scoop made visual inspection difficult. The manufacturer's Engine Manual was also used as a source for the operator's Overhaul Manual. The manufacturer's document referred to cracks in the combustion chamber surface and gave details of crack limits eligible for repair and of suitable repair techniques. These included solution heat-treatment before weld repairs and stress-relief after welding. In the operator's document stress-relief was made optional, dependent on experience, and the solution heat-treatment was deleted for some time before 1985 because of difficulty in implementing it. These changes were approved by the Airworthiness Authority (the CAA).

Fault-finding

The Aircraft maintenance manual contained information on fault diagnosis of the engine when in everyday use, reproduced from the manufacturer's engine maintenance manual. A section covering slow acceleration listed possible symptoms and relevant tests with corrective action. Most of these referred to components of the engine control system; a reference to combustion-chamber shift appeared, but no specific mention of distress such as can cracking. Procedures for a ground run to test and adjust the FCU trim were also given. A limited range of idle adjustment was permitted, according to the engine manufacturers this was largely intended to cure throttle-lever misalignment. Some operators regarded it as unnecessary if the FCU had previously been calibrated on a workshop test rig.

Operator's procedures

The No. 9 can showed a long circumferential crack in the 3/4 liner area, but at that time no length limit for weld repair was stated, and repair of cracks up to a full 360° were regarded as proper. A published crack-length limit was deleted by the engine manufacturer some years before the operator began to use this engine type. The accident investigators discovered that some other operators were imposing limits of their own, at about the original figure stated by the engine manufacturer. This was called a 'burner management' programme, aimed at setting a crack-repair limit contributing to reliable and economic operation of the engine. This programme interacted with the heat-treatment and stress-relief requirements quoted in the overhaul manual of that operator, so that most other operators were not performing the complete set of processes recommended by the engine manufacturer, presumably preferring to scrap damaged cans at some point.

Weld repair

The repair technique recommended for circumferential cracks in the combustion cans was called direct-fusion weld repair, and had been in use for a long time. The operators' experience seemed to indicate that this repair was not recovering can fatigue life. The engine manufacturer had issued warnings, through all-operator communications and meetings, that weld-repaired cans did not have the same fatigue life as new cans or material. The engine manufacturer quoted claimed increases in life from solution heat-treatment before repair. Post-accident tests on specimens concluded that solution heat-treatment at the then recommended temperatures would not improve fatigue resistance, and that post-weld stress-relief was unnecessary in view of the high running temperature of the cans. Omission of these was therefore not thought by the accident investigators to have a significant influence on the can failure.

Other reported incidents

Although very few catastrophic failures of the combustion-chamber outer case had occurred, the number of events where the case became holed or overheated did indicate the existence of a problem. The engine manufacturer regarded these as repair deficiencies or as high-time effects, and did not issue a service bulletin or airworthiness directive for this defect. Elements of the messages issued as advisory communications to operators could be seen, after the accident, to be warnings of potential dangers. These were the relation between slow engine acceleration and combustion can deformation, the fatigue life of weld-repaired cans, and the recommendation to perform X-ray inspection of areas in the cans.

The operator had consulted other users with much longer experience of the engine type and had not received the impression that combustion-can performance was inadequate, nor been informed of 'Burner Management' programmes. The reference in the engine manufacturer's communications to high-time parts was taken by the operator to be inapplicable in their case, because they were comparatively recent buyers of the aircraft.

The accident report did criticise the apparent absence of dialogue between the operator and the engine manufacturer, so that each believed the other was acting in accordance with the content of messages being exchanged, when there was no confirmation of this.

Pilot reports and reaction

Starting an aircraft gas turbine engine is a complex sequence of events, involving manual action by the aircraft commander and monitoring of automatic behaviour in some components. It is not unusual for stages in this process to give trouble, so that reports of starting difficulty are familiar to airline engineers. The JT8D engine used by this operator had a history of slow acceleration; analysis of technical logs showed frequent reports of this and of throttle mismatch in the months leading up to the accident. Action was taken in accordance with the fault-finding section of the aircraft maintenance manual, this meant that can inspection was not considered. The apparently random occurrence of reports for these defects and the response to maintenance action was a further source of confusion, and led to the belief that it was a 'nuisance' defect — something awkward but ineradicable that must be endured.

Conclusion

The accident report considered that the scale of this problem merited a more thorough discussion between the parties than had taken place; this would have cleared up the many misunderstandings that had existed in the meaning of some terms used, the possible reasons for the defects, and the applicability of some maintenance and repair techniques being used or considered.

CHAPTER 8 THE FUTURE OF AIRCRAFT MAINTENANCE

THE FUTURE

The future of aircraft maintenance is closely tied to the future of the air transport industry itself. The past decade has seen many economic, technical and political changes in the industry, some of which will continue to influence events in the next ten years. Discussing these in turn:

Traffic growth

Most forecasts issued recently by aircraft manufacturers and international bodies agree broadly that the industry as a whole will continue to grow, and that this growth will be at a higher annual rate in the 1990s than in the 1980s. Two sets of forecasts are shown here.

These all indicate that volumes of traffic in twenty years time will be several times greater than present levels, even though fuel price increases are expected to be equally dramatic. It may be wondered where all these aircraft are going to land, given the congestion experienced in industrialised nations recently and the strong local community resistance to airport development in these countries. Present under-utilised airports will become important, and technical improvements to the air traffic system should increase its capacity beyond current limits. The trend towards use of larger aircraft at busy airports will continue, though it seems unlikely that 1000-passenger aircraft will appear. As a consequence, the number of aircraft in use will increase, and so will the demand for maintenance skills and facilities.

Table 8.1 Passenger traffic development (Airbus, 1990)
ICAO world and regions (billion RPK) scheduled and non-scheduled

Year	1978	1988	1998	2008
Europe (excl. USSR)	262	419	683	1,031
North America	425	753	1,158	1,709
Latin America	49	82	153	258
Africa	28	43	69	110
Middle East	28	48	82	136
Asia/Pacific	130	315	712	1,367
Total world	922	1,660	2,857	4,611
Annual growth rate				5.5%

Fig. 8.1 Airbus forecast

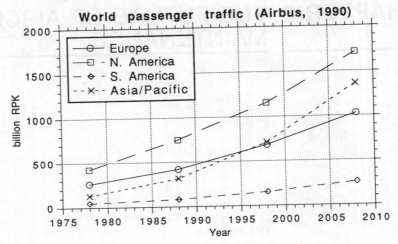

World passenger traffic (Airbus, 1990)

Table 8.2   ICAO scheduled traffic forecasts

	Actual	Actual	Forecast	Average annual growth rate	
				1978−1988	1988−2000
RPK billions	**1978**	**1988**	*2000*	**1978−1988**	*1988−2000*
Total RPK	937	1,696	3,450	6.1%	6.0%
International	385	756	1,740	7.0%	7.0%
Domestic	552	940	1,710	5.5%	5.0%
Passenger millions	**1978**	**1988**	*2000*	**1978−1988**	*1988−2000*
Total passengers	679	1,072	1,945	4.7%	5.0%
International	143	232	480	5.0%	6.0%
Domestic	536	840	1,465	4.6%	4.5%
Freight TK billions	**1978**	**1988**	*2000*	**1978−1988**	*1988−2000*
Total tonne-km	26	54	124	7.5%	7.0%
International	17	41	107	9.3%	8.5%
Domestic	9	12	17	3.2%	3.0%
Freight 1,000 tonnes	**1978**	**1988**	*2000*	**1978−1988**	*1988−2000*
Total freight	11	17	30	5.0%	4.5%
International	4	8	17	7.5%	6.5%
Domestic	7	9	14	3.4%	3.0%

(Displayed figures rounded to nearest integer.)

Privatisation and deregulation

The international airline system founded by the Chicago Convention of 1944 was based mostly on state-owned airlines, except in the USA. This in turn led to the bilateral-agreement method of negotiating traffic rights between countries, using designated carriers. Inside the USA, a system of regulated competition appeared. The Deregulation Act of 1978 removed this, and the following decade saw many changes in the structure of the industry, ending with the formation of very large airline groups owning hundreds of aircraft.

Elsewhere there has been a move towards states divesting themselves of airline ownership, since the formative years of air transport, in which protection might be justified, are over. In Europe the dominant event is expected to be the Single European

Fig. 8.2 ICAO passenger forecast

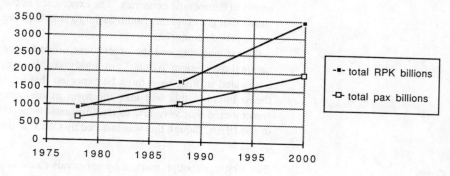

ICAO scheduled passenger traffic forecasts

Fig. 8.3 ICAO freight forecast

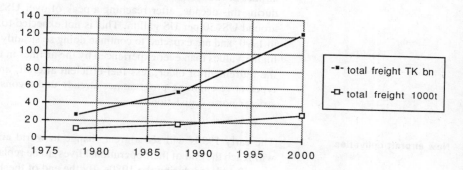

ICAO scheduled freight traffic forecasts

Act in 1993, creating one market without borders. There has been speculation about the extent to which the US experience will be repeated, but most observers expect the transition to a free air-transport market to be less dramatic in Europe.

The combined effect of these forces is to make airlines much more cost-conscious than in the era of regulation and state ownership. Some observers have expressed anxiety that this will adversely affect safety, arguing that operators will try to cut expenditure on training, facilities and research. The evidence from the US history does not support this. It is true that some accidents attributable to maintenance deficiency occurred after deregulation in the USA, but such events also happened before deregulation. The FAA imposed some highly publicised fines on operators for non-compliance, but this appears to have been done partly for political reasons.

The competitive nature of travel markets with this relaxed economic regulation will raise the emphasis on marketing methods by airlines, and make it more important for operators to respond quickly to changes in demand or taste.

Environmental effects

Aircraft use internal combustion engines for propulsion. This has side effects in the form of noise, pollution, and carbon dioxide production. Noise limits to the ICAO Annex 16 Chapter 3 level are expected to be mandatory for most countries by 1990. After that date, no new Chapter 2 aircraft can be bought, but they may remain in use for some time, up to AD 2015 in some proposals. Whether all communities will accept this is doubtful. Aircraft exhaust emissions usually have to comply with the US Environmental Protection Agency (EPA) directives, which specify acceptable values for known causes of environmental damage such as oxides of nitrogen. It is likely that tougher standards will be devised, as anxiety over the environmental effects grows in democratic countries. The experience of the 1970s with fuel price increases shows that governments find it easier to shift the burden of change on to airlines than on to private motorists.

Global warming and the greenhouse effect has become an active topic for international discussion. Aircraft are highly visible and obvious producers of the gases implicated in this, so it must be expected that legislation will appear to deal with them. Possibly this will take the form of fuel consumption targets. It should be remembered that very few of the forecasts in the 1960s predicted the energy crisis of the 1970s, though this was induced by OPEC action rather than just market forces.

Costs

The 1980s, although marked by upheavals caused by the economic aftermath of the oil price shocks in the 1970s and the consequent recession, have been kind to the airlines in one essential resource — the price of fuel. Fig. 8.4 shows that prices declined during this decade, after reaching a peak of over US$1.00 per US gallon, down to around US¢50 per US gallon. This is not expected to last; fuel prices began to rise in 1990, and are expected to continue doing so steadily throughout the 1990s to much higher values than ever experienced by the airlines in the 1970s. This will accelerate the retirement of older, less fuel-efficient aircraft, and increase demand for newer types or re-engining programmes already under consideration for compliance with stricter noise legislation.

New aircraft deliveries

The early 1990s will see a great change in world airline fleets. Many old aircraft will reach the end of their operational lives, to be replaced by new higher-technology aircraft ordered during the 1980s. By the end of the 1990s, the delivery rate of new types in the smaller sizes will have slowed down, but deliveries of large aircraft will actually increase. These new aircraft will demand different maintenance skills from their predecessors, particularly in avionics, control systems, and materials. The reliability and maintainability of these aircraft is expected to be better than that of previous types. Operators will have to improve their planning skills to take advantage of this.

Old aircraft maintenance

The present generation of old aircraft will continue in use for some time, after the ageing aircraft programmes devised to restore them have been implemented. The final retirement of these aircraft may be determined by economic or legal factors; estimated maximum ages of aircraft have been revised upwards on several occasions in the past

Fig. 8.4 Fuel price history

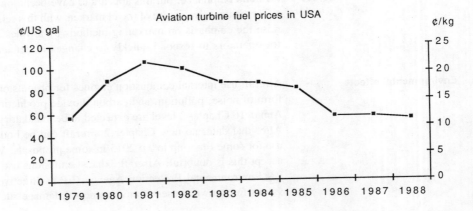

so prediction is uncertain. Some leasing companies have quoted aircraft lives of up to 30 years, in their promotions to prospective investors. Supply of spares for some types may become difficult, as manufacturers prefer to concentrate on new types. Operators or maintenance organisations may have to consider entering the spares production business. This experience is already known to military aircraft users; possibly they could sell this expertise to civilian customers.

Skills and labour shortages

In most Western industrial nations, there is concern over a reduction in entries to the labour market. This is due to two factors, a decline in the proportion of young people in populations, and a decrease in those taking science subjects at school. Already some UK employers have experienced difficulty in recruitment. The table from the UK CAA, in Fig. 8.5, shows another effect.

In view of this, airline engineering employers should seriously examine their requirements for skilled labour. De-skilling of some routine jobs may be possible; in the past employers have been reluctant to tackle this because of the industrial-relations damage that could result, and because a ready supply of skilled labour was available. Civilian employers have relied on the military for trained specialists, but if the 'peace dividend' of reduction in forces stationed in Europe leads to a contraction in this source, alternatives will have to be found. There is a strong possibility that the maintenance work will go to countries with a suitable workforce if it cannot be performed at home.

Another difficulty is that the nature of airline employment is changing — it is no longer as 'exclusive' as it was in the early days. The advent of mass travel for everyone has diminished the unique attraction of the traditional staff-travel perquisite for airline employees. In a more competitive market, the job security enjoyed in the heyday of IATA fare-fixing and government-backed low-interest loans or subsidies has also disappeared for many airline employees. A side effect of this is that employers can no longer insist on such restrictive conditions for qualification or promotion. Many airline engineering functions are already closely specified by airworthiness regulations, and imposing additional requirements will make prospective entrants query the need for the study time involved.

Technologies

Aircraft will continue to require maintenance in the future. The importance of weight saving for economic reasons makes this inevitable as a design factor, and with the introduction of new technology it is likely that unexpected problems will require

Fig. 8.5 CAA aircraft maintenance engineer licencing

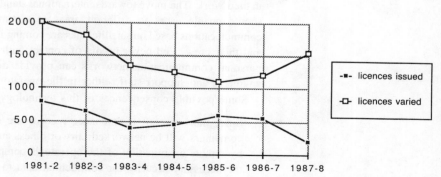

CAA Aircraft maintenance engineer licensing

- ■ licences issued
- □ licences varied

modification after delivery. Maintenance engineers will therefore need the ability to identify faults in equipment and to negotiate with suppliers for corrective action.

Among the technologies expected to have an impact in the future are:

— composite materials in structures;
— non-metallic materials in engines;
— 'one-piece' manufacturing methods;
— automation and software in avionics;
— active systems for stability and control;
— environmental effects of processes used in manufacture or maintenance;
— computers, communications, and information technology.

Many of these will pose new and unusual problems in fault diagnosis, repair, and maintenance. Composite materials have been in use for many years as secondary structural components, but are now becoming part of the primary aircraft structure. The consequences of failure to detect deterioration and arrest it will therefore be more serious. In view of the number of occasions when failure of even traditional metal structures did not occur in accordance with the designers' assumptions, it follows that there is still much to be learned about composites technology, as its practitioners readily admit.

Increasing use of automatic control systems for safety-critical or non-essential purposes, coupled with the trend to digital systems and programmable devices, will require the ability to distinguish hardware from software faults. Digital technology is now sufficiently well established for a working knowledge of its principles to be common among operators' staff, but the rate of change is still quite rapid. The trend towards high reliability in solid-state equipment is accompanied by manufacturing methods that are deemed 'non-repairable', but operators often take a different view when faced with the recommended replacement of a complete module. Thus repair of multi-layer circuit boards is accepted as necessary, so no doubt further ingenuity will become evident.

It is the operators' experience, civil or military, that the introduction of any new manufacturing process is such a preoccupation with its originators that repair techniques get lower priority. The user often has to take the initiative in finding or devising suitable schemes and obtaining the approval from authorities.

Computers and communications

The use of information technology in aircraft maintenance has already been referred to in this book. This has made significant improvements to routine data processing for business and technical records, to the extent that many organisations would now be unable to function without computer systems. There will be further growth in the use of computers and communications to assist authorities, organisations, and engineers in their work. The move towards international standards for networking and software should enable users in different areas to communicate more effectively. New communications based on satellite links are coming into use, which means that aircraft and their crew need never be out of contact with their main base. The growth in personal communication networks can provide direct links between maintenance engineers and support staff, either in the operator, or at the manufacturer.

Some possible consequences of this technology could be:

Since most aircraft maintenance records are stored on a computer, and most computers will be networked, airworthiness authorities could check compliance by remote examination of the operator's computer system. This would require the necessary security for confidential data to be imposed.

Onboard maintenance systems can transmit data direct to base, allowing staff engineers to discuss fault-finding with the crew and forewarning line maintenance engineers of the action required.

Maintenance engineers on the ramp can contact base staff directly. With the type of lightweight video equipment now available and high-speed data links, visual examination of the problem can be shared by people at different locations. Use of on-line maintenance manuals enables all participants to agree about the basic information being consulted.

Extension of inventory-control systems to contractors and manufacturers will provide complete tracking of parts. Knowledge of progress in the repair circuit will benefit 'just-in-time' methods and reduce inventory levels.

Computer-aided planning using techniques not previously possible will allow more examination of alternatives in the search to find the best plan, and faster response to changes produced by external events.

Maintenance staff will have to learn new skills in the access and manipulation of data at volumes and speeds much higher than possible with manual systems. Computer staff will have to learn more about the realities of dealing with non-specialist users. Graphical interfaces are being touted as the solution in the next generation of computers, but study of the contenders suggests they have just as much scope for confusion as their predecessors. Hardware and software rarely seems to have received the kind of industrial design lavished on such mundane items as office furniture, for instance.

Safety

As indicated in Chapter 1, the civil air transport safety rate has improved gradually over the years. This has almost matched the rate of increase in traffic, so that the total of annual fatalities has remained nearly constant, with the random fluctuations expected of such an infrequent event.

One serious accident to a single large aircraft can now produce a bad year's result for the whole world industry. Maintenance lapses and design or manufacturing faults, which maintenance engineers might be able to anticipate, are not now the main causes

Fig. 8.6 World air transport accidents and trend (excludes sabotage, hijack, military action)

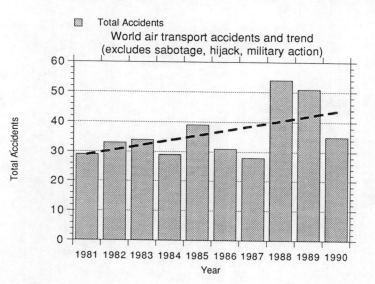

□ Total Accidents

World air transport accidents and trend
(excludes sabotage, hijack, military action)

of most accidents. Even so, it is essential that everyone in the industry makes the greatest effort to continue the improvement in safety.

The reason for this, as one industry member has pointed out, is that reporting of an increasing number of accidents will harm its reputation. Media attention given to even the slightest technical incident involving an aircraft is often out of all proportion to the risks, and this is one of the problems the air transport industry will have to endure if it cannot educate people. Perhaps the novelty of aviation has still not worn off; the accident rate of a relatively low-technology vehicle like the private automobile, with mostly unskilled drivers, seems to be accepted with equanimity because 'everybody does it'.

Improvement in air transport safety by maintenance engineers will have to come from better understanding of the materials, processes and equipment used; from better communications between users, manufacturers and regulators; and from better methods in design, testing and certification. These are all part of current activity by the participants in the industry, but they will also have to be made against a background of improvements in operating costs, higher quality of service to the passenger, political debate about freedom to fly, and concern about security from international terrorism.

The question of 'safety versus economy' nearly always arises when regulators seek to improve the efficiency of the industry by allowing more competition, or even by deregulating the commercial side entirely. As stated before in this chapter, the experience in the USA, which has the most deregulated air transport industry, does not bear this out. Air safety continued to improve in the USA after deregulation. It is up to the airworthiness authorities to sustain their vigilance in the changed circumstances of commercial deregulation. A more serious effect of deregulation may be the high staff turnover, as companies are reformed in the quest for a 'global airline'. Despite the high level of documentation in aircraft maintenance, many practices are not written down, but are learnt by experience or passed on by word.

REFERENCES

BOOKS

Doganis, R. (1985) Flying Off Course — The Economics of International Airlines. George Allen & Unwin 0-04-387005-8.

Grover, J.H.H. (1990) Airline Route Planning. BSP, 0-632-02324-4.

Middleton, D.H. (Gen. Ed) (1989) Avionic Systems. Longman.

Middleton, D.H. (Gen. Ed) (1990) Composite Materials in Aircraft Structures. Longman.

Ramsden, J.M. (1976) The Safe Airline. Macdonald & Jane's.

Ramsden, J.M. (1981) Caring for the Mature Jet. Plaistow Press.

Smith, M.J.T. (1989) Aircraft Noise. Cambridge UP 0-521-33186-2.

Taneja, N.K. (1988) The International Airline Industry. Lexington 0-669-16167-5.

Taylor, L. (1988) Air Travel: How Safe Is It? BSP 0-632-02332-5.

PUBLICATIONS

AIB (Feb 1979) Boeing 707 321C G-BEBP, Lusaka International Airport, Zambia, May 1977. AAR 9/78.

AIB (Dec 1988) Boeing 737-236 G-BGJL, Manchester International Airport, Aug 1985. AAR 8/88.

ATA/IATA (Mar 1983) Airline Industry Standard World Airlines Technical Operations Glossary. WATOG.

BA (June 1986—90) Annual Reports and Accounts.

BAA Annual Reports.

CAA (Jul 1978) Condition Monitored Maintenance: an explanatory handbook. CAP 418.

CAA (Nov 1982) Air Operators' Certificates — Arrangements for Engineering Support. CAP 360 Part Two.

CAA (Aug 1985) Reliability of In-service Inspection of Transport Aircraft Structures. Paper 85013.

CAA (Apr 1986) Section L Licensing — Aircraft Maintenance Engineers. CAP 468.

CAA (Feb 1990) Registration, certification and maintenance of aircraft. CAP 396.

CAA (Apr 1990) Extended range twin operations. CAP 513.

CAA (Jun 1990) UK Airlines: annual operating, traffic and financial statistics 1989. CAP 568.

CAA (Sep 1990) Master Minimum Equipment Lists. CAP 549.

CSO (series) Monthly Digest of Statistics.

CSO (Sep 1989) Key Data 1989/90 Edition.

IATA (July 1989) Annual World Air Transport Statistics.

NAO (1989) Ministry of Defence, Reliability and Maintainability of Defence Equipment. HMSO.

References

NTSB (14 Jun 1989) Aircraft Accident Report: Aloha Airlines, Flight 243 Boeing 737-200, N73711, Near Maui, Hawaii, 28 April 1988. NTSB/AAR-89/03.

SAE (Feb 1988) Guide to Life Usage Monitoring and Parts Management for Aircraft Gas Turbine Engines. AIR 1872.

SAE (Mar 1984) Guide to Oil System Monitoring in Aircraft Gas Turbine Engines. AIR 1828.

SAE (Oct 1986) A Guide to Aircraft Turbine Engine Vibration Monitoring Systems. AIR 1839.

CITY UNIVERSITY AIR TRANSPORT ENGINEERING FINAL YEAR PROJECTS

Barnes, S. (1989) The Electronic Office.

Bertrand, T.J. (1990) Aircraft Weight Control.

Brown, P.J. (1987) Engine Oil Debris Analysis.

Chan, D.C.H. (1990) Cost of Mandatory Modifications.

Chawla, J. (1989) The Sale of Aircraft Surplus Spares.

Elgy, R.D. (1983) Engine Vibration Monitoring on the Spey.

Evans, J.R. (1984) An Analysis of the Current Royal Air Force Practice of Aircraft Structural Fatigue Management.

Gallop, K. (1985) Extended-Range Operation of Twin-Engined Commercial Air Transport Aircraft.

Ganase, K.M. (1984) Microbiological Contamination and Corrosion of Aircraft Integral Fuel Tanks.

Hoban, P.J. (1990) Inspection of Engineering Spares within British Airways.

Holburn, K.J. (1983) The New Generation of Built-in Test Equipment.

Leeks, A.R. (1990) Operating Techniques to Reduce Engine Costs.

Martland, J. (1989) Repair Provisioning Models for the RAF.

Mason, S.P. (1983) Meeting the Boeing 757 test requirements in BA.

Mkoloma, F.K. (1985) Criteria for Aircraft Choice.

Mullen, W.D. (1990) Engineering — Big Business for the Future.

Rogan, E. (1987) The Aircraft Communication Addressing and Reporting System (ACARS).

Young, J.A. (1985) The Concept of Quality Circles and its Applicability in Aircraft Maintenance Engineering.

JOURNALS

Anon. (1989) Certification of Australian registered aircraft — the CAA position. Australian Aviation, May, 120–1.

Bradbury, S.J. (1984) MSG-3 as viewed by the manufacturer (was it effective?). SAE Paper 841482, 1–12.

Brett, L.F. (1984) Integration of MSG-3 into airline operation. SAE Paper 841483.

Bruce, D.A. (1989) Non-destructive evaluation for mature aircraft. AeroTech '89, C398/27, No. 3.

Collinge, K. (1987) TEXMAS — An expert system for gas turbine diagnosis and more. SAE Paper 871737, 1–7.

Cownie, J. (1989) Keeping the senior citizens on the wing. *Professional Engineer*, Vol. 2, No. 8, 32–3.

Cownie, J. (1990) Staged Approach of the Friendly Jet. *Professional Engineer*, Vol. 3, No. 7, 42–4.

Craig, D.K. (1986) Airline engineering role in the management of safety. ICAS 15th Congress, Vol. 2, 1010–16.

Crawford, P.J. (1986) Managing Airworthiness. ICAS 15th Congress, Vol. 2, 532–5.

References

Daniel, D.W. (1987) Reliability and life cycle costs of military aircraft — the vital link. Part 1 — the context. Reliability '87, 3B/3/1—4.

Day, Stahr (1979) A Technique for Engine Maintenance Cost Forecasting. SAE Paper 79-7007, 45—52.

Evans, G.B. (1985) Design Against Corrosion. *Aerospace*, Vol. 12, No. 9, 23—34.

Fairhead, I.F. (1987) Current Capabilities of NDT — a Service Operator's View. *Aerospace*, Vol. 14, No. 2, 17—20.

Finch, D. (1989) Caring for the ageing jets. *Aerospace*, Vol. 16, No. 12, 14—16.

Fitzgerald, K. (1989) Probing Boeing's crossed connections. IEEE Spectrum, May, 30—6.

Frantzen, C. (1990) The 'Euro C of A'. *Aerospace*, Vol. 17, No. 9, 14—18.

Heath, W.G. (1988) Concepts of unreliability underlying the factor of safety for aircraft structures. *Aeronautical Journal*, Vol. 92, No. 911, 1—3.

Hennigs, N.E. (1990) Aging Airplanes. Boeing Airliner, Jul—Sep, 17—20.

Hurcombe, M. (1990) Efficient defence. *Aerospace*, Vol. 17, No. 4, 10—12.

Jagger, D.H. (1989) A320 — Past Definitions and Future Possibilities. *Aerospace*, Vol. 15, No. 9, 8—14.

James, D.O.N. (1988) The use of reliability techniques in civil aircraft structural airworthiness — a CAA view. *Aeronautical Journal*, Vol. 92, No. 911, 3—5.

John, S. (1987) Engineering's Contribution to a Successful Airline. *Aerospace*, Vol. 14, No. 8, 40—4.

Keskey, L.J. (1987) Expert systems in aircraft maintenance training. WESTEX-87, 50—6.

Krapp, A. (1987) Design decisions to increase despatch reliability. AeroTech '87, S/589, No. 2.

Lucas, H. (1987) Introduction and application of the General Electric turbine engine monitoring software within KLM Royal Dutch Airlines. ASME Paper 87-GT-167, 1—6.

March, P.R. (1989) Keeping the Tornado Flying. RAF Yearbook 1989, 28—32.

Martin, A.J. (1989) Development of Onboard Maintenance Systems on Boeing Airplanes. *Aerospace*, Vol. 16, No. 8, 16—21.

Murphy, E. (1989) Ageing aircraft: too old to fly? IEEE Spectrum, June. 28—31.

Nakata, D. (1984) An introduction to MSG-3. SAE Paper 841481.

Pearse, P. (1990) Hands-on maintenance managers. *Aerospace*, Vol. 17, No. 6, 20—1.

Peckett, D.S. (1987) Engineering IT on RAF operational stations. AeroTech '87, S/599, No. 1.

Pettigrew, J. (1987) Gas turbine engine monitoring systems — helicopter experience. SAE Paper 871735, 1—15.

Phillips, M.J. (1989) Maintenance of Concorde into the 21st Century. AeroTech '89, C398/27, No. 1.

Pollak, G. (1990) Computer Assisted Optimisation of Maintenance Activities. *Aircraft Engineering*, Jun, 24—7.

Pontecorvo, J. (1984) MSG-3 — A method for maintenance program planning. SAE Paper 841485.

Punches, K. (1983) Airplane Reliability in a Nutshell. IEEE Trans. *Reliability*, Vol. R-32, No. 2, 130—3.

Ramsden, J.M. (1990) Maintenance efficiency. *Aerospace*, Vol. 17, No. 2, 18—20.

Ratcliffe, G. (1988) The Ground Engineer's Lot. *Aerospace*, Vol. 15, No. 9, 14—21.

Rose, J. (1986) Maintainability Optimisation — the Future Challenge. ICAS 15th Congress, Vol. 2, 697—702.

Saith, A. (1987) In-situ cumulative damage assessment in turbine wheels. SAE Paper 871785, 1—7.

Saull, J.W. (1987) Objectives of Maintenance — Airworthiness. *Aerospace*, Vol. 14, No. 7, 41—7.

Saunders, D.E. (1987) Analytical R&M methods applied to forecasting engine logistics requirements. ASME Paper 87-GT-40, 1—6.

Sawtell, R.M. (1988) Avionic system integration using the Beta Box. *GEC Review*, Vol. 4, No. 2, 94—9.

References

Schurter, W. (1989) The Maintenance Philosophy of a Civil Operator. *Aerospace*, Vol. 16, No. 9, 6–11.

Serghides, V.C., Fielding, J.P. (1987) A reliability and maintainability prediction methodology for the conceptual aircraft design process. Reliability '87, 2A/1/1–11.

Skinner, G. (1989) Maintaining mature military aircraft. AeroTech '89, C398/27, No. 2.

Smith, R. (1989) Improving the cost-effectiveness of airframe inspection. AeroTech '89, C398/27, No. 4.

Stone, D.E.W. (1988) The reliability of inspection techniques in relation to damage tolerant design. *Aeronautical Journal*, Vol. 92, No. 911, 5–8.

Tester, R.M. (1990) System Considerations for Integrated Machinery Health Monitoring. *GEC Review*, Vol. 5, No. 3, 140–50.

Thorn, J. (1989) Industry putting pressure on CAA to streamline certification procedures. Australian Aviation, Jan, 36–42.

Trotter, K. (1989) Avionic software support in the Royal Air Force. AeroTech '89, C398/17, No. 2.

Wakely, B. (1987) Military aerospace maintenance — IT strategy for the future. AeroTech '87, S/598, No. 3.

Warren, D.V. (1987) Passenger Cabin Safety — CAA Airworthiness Requirements. *Aerospace*, Vol. 14, No. 11, 7–10.

— (1990) High Speed Envair Project for the RAF. *Aircraft Engineering*, Apr, 28.

MAGAZINE ARTICLES

Bailey, J. (23/9/89) FAA issues Douglas ageing proposals. *Flight International*, 26–27.

Boot, W. (1/2/90) The accidental journalist. *Columbia Journalism Review*, 17–21.

Brownlie, A. (1/4/89) OMEGA Update 1989. *British Airways Engineering*, 10–12.

Condom, P. (1/6/88) The SMART way to cut the costs of avionics maintenance. *Interavia*, 605–6.

Daly, K. (21/1/89) Firespray. *Flight International*, 42–6.

Daly, K. (9/9/89) Carriers prepare for Combi directive. *Flight International*, 8.

Davis, L. (1/7/90) Retirees' help may be needed. *Air Transport World*, 140.

Donoghue, J.A. (1/2/88) Unions fight, delay fix for foreign repair station hassle. *Air Transport World*, 16–18.

Donoghue, J.A. (1/5/90) Debugging the new whale (B747-400). *Air Transport World*, 41–4.

Feldman, J.M. (1/2/88) Product Support: Promises, promises. *Air Transport World*, 25–31.

Fletcher, M. (4/2/89) MoD attacked over £1bn cost of poor military equipment. *The Times*.

Flint, P. (1/1/89) Old planes, new money. *Air Transport World*, 52–6.

Flint, P. (1/6/90) The joy of leasing. *Air Transport World*, 24–6.

Flint, P. (1/7/89) Brother, can you spare a dime? *Air Transport World*, 101–4.

Flint, P. (1/2/90) The word on the street is 'sell'. *Air Transport World*, 63–6.

Fotos, C.P. (28/8/89) Acoustic Emission Technique Tests Aircraft Integrity. *Aviation Week*, 76.

Fotos, C.P. (18/9/89) Task Force Outlines Fixes for Aging Douglas Fleet. *Aviation Week*, 122–3.

Fotos, C.P. (9/10/89) Flight safety advances hinge on pilot-management teamwork. *Aviation Week*, 31–2.

Fotos, C.P. (2/4/90) Proposed Corrosion Control Program Targets Boeing Commercial Aircraft. *Aviation Week*, 57–8.

Gaines, M. (10/1/90) Engineering a Crisis. *Flight International*, 38–40.

Geisenheyner (30/4/88) How Reliable? *Flight International*, 45–8.

Goold, I. (18/4/90) In the shadow of Aloha. *Flight International*, 35–8.

References

Henderson, D. (1/2/89) Airlines, FAA intensify old transport efforts. *Air Transport World*, 61−5.

Henderson, D. (1/2/89) USAir unveils affordable automated M&E control system. *Air Transport World*, 79−80.

Henderson, D. (1/7/89) Plastic media: Nontoxic solution to dry-stripping. *Air Transport World*, 95−6.

Hughes, D. (24/7/89) United DC-10 Crashes in Sioux City, Iowa. *Aviation Week*, 96−7.

Hughes, D. (16/10/89) ICAO Assembly Fails to Agree on Aircraft Noise Restrictions. *Aviation Week*, 82−3.

Kandebo, S.W. (14/5/90) Launch of Rolls' Re-engining Plan Poses Challenge to JT8D Hushkits. *Air Transport World*, 112.

Learmount, D. (15/10/88) Management by radio (ACARS). *Flight International*, 38−41.

Learmount, D. (25/2/89) Sharing Spanners. *Flight International*, 26−8.

Learmount, D. (22/7/89) Europe ahead on safety? *Flight International*, 44−6.

Learmount, D. (29/7/89) Boeing works on JAR 747-400 requirements. *Flight International*, 45.

Learmount, D. (29/7/89) Engine breakup suspected in DC-10 crash. *Flight International*, 4.

Learmount, D. (16/9/89) Aloha accident made age an issue. *Flight International*, 29−30.

Learmount, D. (15/11/89) Climbing into the future. *Flight International*, 32−4.

Learmount, D. (18/4/90) Europe faces air traffic chaos, says IATA. *Flight International*, 6.

Lefer, H. (1/2/89) Carriers refine materials systems to meet tighter MEL standards. *Air Transport World*, 88−93.

Lefer, H. (1/11/89) Getting old but not ready to retire. *Air Transport World*, 59−60.

Lefer, H. (1/11/89) 'Who'll fix the ageing aircraft? *Air Transport World*, 101−2.

Lefer, H. (1/7/90) Hushkitting: The prudent alternative. *Air Transport World*, 107−10.

Lynn, N. (26/8/89) Sensitive skins. *Flight International*, 34−6.

McClenahen, J. (1/12/89) The impact of air crashes. *Air Transport World*, 71−4.

McKenna, J.T. (2/7/90) Higher Maintenance Standards Sought for World's Aging Fleet. *Aviation Week*, 60−3.

Mecham, M. (28/8/89) Sioux City DC-10 Accident May Force Extensive Inspection of CF6 Engines. *Aviation Week*, 28−9.

Moorman, R.W. (1/5/90) Brave new world (labor relations). *Air Transport World*, 107.

Norris, G. (1/3/89) Qualitair: A new force in maintenance. *Interavia*, 258−9.

Norris, G. (24/1/90) Helicopter Health and Safety. *Flight International*, 26−9.

O'Lone, R.G. (24/7/89) Ageing Aircraft Issue Presents Major Challenge to Industry. *Aviation Week*, 42−5.

O'Lone, R.G. (24/7/89) Airframe Makers Use Aging Aircraft Experience to Refine Design Practices. *Aviation Week*, 94−5.

O'Lone, R.G. (24/7/89) Economics, not Safety, is Key Issue in Replacement of Older Transport. *Aviation Week*, 69−77.

O'Lone, R.G. (24/7/89) Government, Industry Mount Major Effort to Characterize Aging Aircraft Issues. *Aviation Week*, 60−??.

O'Lone, R.G. (24/7/89) Strong Earnings Enable Airlines to Finance Fleet Expansion. *Aviation Week*, 85.

O'Lone, R.G. (5/3/90) Boeing Increases Long-Range Market Estimate by $110 Billion. *Aviation Week*, 31.

O'Lone, R.G. (12/3/90) Boeing forms special unit to boost 747-400 reliability. *Aviation Week*, 68−9.

Ott, J. (20/6/88) Independent research urged for inspection, maintenance. *Aviation Week*, 112−??.

Ott, J. (9/10/89) 10 fatal crashes spark call for new safety measures. *Aviation Week*, 28−30.

Ott, J. (16/4/90) Board finds that United, FAA and Boeing contributed to 747 accident near Hawaii. *Air Transport World*, 68−9.

References

Ramsden, J.M. (30/8/86) The Inspectable Structure. *Flight International*, 113–16.
Reed, A. (1/7/88) Looking at European maintenance. *Air Transport World*, 83–4.
Reed, A. (1/2/89) Qualitair hopes airlines cast off maintenance. *Air Transport World*, 85–6.
Reed, A. (1/3/89) European airlines decry penalties of Chapter 2 noise rule. *Air Transport World*, 32–40.
Reed, A. (1/5/90) Airbus: 10,000 jets by the century's end. *Air Transport World*, 48–50.
Reingold, L. (1/4/90) TCAS at the turning point. *Air Transport World*, 44–52.
Rek, B. (1/6/88) Foreign repair stations raise passions at Amtech 88. *Interavia*, 599–??.
Rek, B. (1/5/90) Innovations appear on airliner finance scene. *Interavia*, 391–3.
Sutton, O. (1/5/90) Europe's Airlines on the Brink: All blocked up. *Interavia*, 381.
Sutton, O. (1/5/90) Europe's Airlines on the Brink: Nationals dig in. *Interavia*, 378–80.
Sweetman, W. (1/3/89) Life with the older aircraft. *Interavia*, 250–4.
Vandyk, A. (1/3/89) Simplified English makes reading technical manuals easier. *Air Transport World*, 84.
Vandyk, A. (1/10/89) ILO expects sharp changes for airline employees. *Air Transport World*, 112.
Warwick, G. (30/8/86) A320: fly-by-wire airliner. *Flight International*, 86–93.
Whittington (1/4/90) Data links and critical red (ACAMS). *Air Transport World*, 65–6.
Wilson, J.A.R. (1/5/89) Traders ponder jets' age and noise problems. *Interavia*, 433–4.
Wilson, J.A.R. (1/12/89) Caring for the elderly jet. *Interavia*, 1177–9.
Winn, A. (23/9/89) Ageing study cites 18 changes for BAC One-Eleven. *Flight International*, 26–7.
(1/7/89) 747 delivery JARred. *Air Transport World*, 6.
(15/1/90) GAO Wants FAA to develop Central Plan for Ensuring Safety of Ageing Aircraft. *Aviation Week*, 66–7.
(21/3/90) Burbank hushes Heavylift 707s. *Flight International*, 16.
(2/7/90) New Regulations, Surplus Will Force Narrow-Body Transports Out of Service. *Aviation Week*, 73–7.
(1/7/89) $142 million facelift proposed for old planes. *Air Transport World*, 6.
(14/3/90) FAA orders major structural modifications to ageing Boeings. *Flight International*, 11.
(18/4/90) Senior citizens. *Flight International*, 41–5.
(2/7/90) Task Force Recommends Easing Proposed ADs to Increase Flexibility. *Aviation Week*, 64–6.
(2/7/90) Shortage of Replacement Parts May Delay Ageing Aircraft Repairs. *Aviation Week*, 68–72.
(2/7/90) Boeing, Douglas Alter Design Approach to Control Corrosion. *Aviation Week*, 78.
(1/1/89) FAR 145 foreign repair station dispute resolved. *Interavia*, 14.
(9/7/90) US Military Equipment Surplus Grows as Worldwide Weapons Market Shrinks. *Aviation Week*, 52–3.
(4/6/88) Harris develops expert maintainer. *Flight International*, 16.
(1/11/88) Why do I need computer systems? *British Airways Engineering*, 7–10.
(21/5/90) Airline Uses Airborne Data-Link Systems to Improve Operational Management, Reliability. *Aviation Week*, 38.
(21/5/90) Air Canada Draws on Experience for A320 Maintenance Program. *Aviation Week*, 42–3.
(10/6/89) SAA 747 wreckage examined in detail. *Flight International*, 48.
(28/8/89) Aloha Airlines Probe Raises Questions About FAA Surveillance of Maintenance. *Aviation Week*, 77–80.
(4/9/89) Investigators Detail Failure of Aloha 737's Fuselage. *Aviation Week*, 76–8.
(11/9/89) NTSB Probes Aloha 737's Maintenance Records. *Aviation Week*, 131–4.
(18/9/89) Aloha 737 Fuselage Skin, Structures Undergo Detailed Fatigue Inspection. *Aviation Week*, 129–30.
(25/3/89) UK accident investigators want fire-hard fuselages. *Flight International*, 20–4.
(13/5/89) US Navy bans Kapton. *Flight International*, 4.

References

(25/9/89) Safety Board Examines Aloha's Maintenance of Ageing 737s. *Aviation Week*, 117–21.

(9/10/89) Safety Board analyses how Aloha 737 fuselage failed. *Aviation Week*, 145–9.

(23/10/89) Safety Board urges FAA to revamp maintenance, inspection training. *Aviation Week*, 77–84.

(13/11/89) NTSB urges increase in frequency of fatigue testing of transports. *Aviation Week*, 83–6.

INDEX